Country Childhoods

Geoffrey Dutton was born in South Australia in 1922 and educated at Geelong and Adelaide, and at Magdalen College, Oxford

A distinguished writer and editor, he is the author of many books including historical biographies, art and literary criticism, travel writing, seven collections of poetry, short stories, and stories for children, as well as several novels. He has also worked as literary editor for publishing houses, newspapers and journals, and has served on the boards of various cultural organisations. In 1976 he was awarded the Order of Australia. Geoffrey Dutton now lives in the Glasshouse Mountains region of Queensland.

Country
Childhoods

Edited by
Geoffrey Dutton

University of Queensland Press

First published 1992 by University of Queensland Press
Box 42, St Lucia, Queensland 4067 Australia

Typeset by University of Queensland Press
Printed in Australia by The Book Printer, Victoria

Distributed in the USA and Canada by
International Specialized Book Services, Inc.,
5602 N.E. Hassalo Street, Portland, Oregon 97213-3640

 Creative writing program assisted by
the Australia Council, the Australian
Government's arts funding and
advisory body

Australia Council
for the Arts

Cataloguing in Publication Data
National Library of Australia

Country childhoods.
  1. Short stories, Australian. 2. Authors, Australian — 20th century —
  Biography — Youth. I. Dutton, Geoffrey, 1922-   .

A823.0830891734

ISBN 0 7022 2434 0

Contents

Acknowledgments

For permission to reproduce stories in this collection, acknowledgment is made to Alex Buzo for "Armidale: No Palo Alto"; to Cameron Creswell Agency Pty Ltd for "A Country Childhood" by Roger McDonald; to Chatto & Windus for "Over the Bump" by Joan Colebrook from *A House of Trees*, 1988; to Margaret Coombs for "Black Sheep"; to Curtis Brown (Aust.) Pty Ltd for "You Will Know His Creatures" by Susan Johnson; to Max Fatchen and the *Advertiser* for "Waterbag Summers and Draughthorse Dawns"; to Hodder & Stoughton Ltd for "A Little Candle Burning in the Night" by Phyllis Gant from *Islands*, 1973; to Colin Thiele for "Sunrise and Starshine" from *The Early Dreaming* compiled by Michael Dugan, 1980; to McPhee Gribble Publishers for "Childhood Days" by Elsie Roughsey, editor Paul Memmott, from *An Aboriginal Mother Tells of the Old and New*, 1984, and for "The Woodheap" by Jean Bedford from *Country Girl Again and Other Stories*, 1985, and for "The First House" by Dorothy Hewett from *Wildcard*, 1990; to Craig McGregor for "Goin' Back to Gundagai"; to Sally McInerney for "The Disappearance of Conlan's Swamp"; to Ian Moffitt for "A Good Rexona Town"; to Penguin Books Australia Ltd for "You Are My Sunshine" by Ruby Langford from *Don't Take Your Love to Town*, 1988, and for "Inside and Outside" by Suzanne Falkiner from *Rain in the Distance*, 1986; to Peter Skrzynecki for "The Day that Lasted Forever"; to University of Queensland Press for "I Want a Shilling Too" by David Campbell from *Evening Under Lamplight*, 1976, and for "Mothers and Old Lovers" by Gillian Mears from *Fineflour*, 1990.

Introduction

"Country children know more than they know", wrote Randolph Stow in a poem, when he was himself scarcely more than a child. So of course do city children, quick and streetwise, but their knowledge is not sharpened or made uneasy by the nearness of Nature. Human nature, yes, but the loneliness (and often the blessed company) of that further, ancient Nature is close even to country towns.

This collection of country childhoods includes both Aboriginal and white (whether migrant or local), coming from farm, bush or country town. The pieces are so varied that it would be foolish to attempt to generalise about them. Yet they form a company in which each would recognise the other, whether rich or poor, black or white. A possum or a snake would not surprise them, nor a flood or a fire.

The narrowness and gossip of country towns is legendary, and the sleepiness, but the children inside the towns and further out seem to share a freedom, whatever their background.

There's no denying that the freedom is characteristically Australian, harsh, maybe, but not hedged. The Aborigines, of course, had special problems, for theirs was basically a loss of freedom. But even so, they have had a marvellous ability not just to make the best of it, but to take great sustenance from however little they were given. They are the original children of the country, and it remains truly theirs. Nevertheless, it is amazing how quickly those of the white invaders who wanted to love the country, sent deep roots into the new land. There is no presence here of that fashionable alienation that claims that we Australians don't really belong to this country.

The Aborigines, of course, were never bored with living in

the country. This is the privilege of the city dweller, epitomised by Dr Johnson's remark that living in the country is "a kind of mental imprisonment". It can also be the penalty of the child who has grown up in the country but longs to escape.

But while the early freedom lasts, perhaps one could risk a generalisation, and say that a confidence in belonging is common to all these childhoods. This applies even to those like Alex Buzo or Ian Moffitt in whom a witty sense of the incongruous keeps any tendency to mythologise at bay.

Indeed, all these pieces are history rather than myth. There is no lack of imagination, but a strong affinity with truth.

Geoffrey Dutton
November, 1991

Starting on our Block

Don Munday

With a bit of help from the rest of us, Dad soon got a tent up.
Then he leant some sheets of iron on the windward side of the
fire so we could sit around it in reasonable comfort. The table
was set up, and Mum started to get the cooking and eating
utensils sorted out. By now it was close to sundown, so Dad,
Charlie and Jack went out to shoot some twenty-eight parrots. It wasn't long before they returned with ten birds, which
were soon plucked and got ready for the pot.

Everyone was up bright and early next morning. There
were plenty of birds about, but no signs of animal life —
though we'd heard dingo howls and possum noises during the
night. We weren't long over breakfast that first morning —
porridge, bread, jam and the usual billy tea. Mum and Dad
left Charlie in charge of us kids as they went off to find a suitable site for a house. It wasn't long before they were back —
they'd found a nice glade in a patch of morrell saplings only
about twenty chains from the camp.

We were all set to work clearing a track to the future
homestead. In those times, when a settler was granted land
he was given a freehold homestead site — a block of 160
acres. If at any later date he wanted to borrow money for
"carry-on", the homestead block was never included in the
mortgage. We spent all day making the track, and also doing
a bit of clearing work around the home site.

The next day Dad walked to the Lee brothers' farm at
Kirk's Rock. It was mail day, a weekly service from the
Wickepin Post Office. Bill Downs was the mailman, and he
would also bring out stores if people asked him to. On mail
day Kirk's Rock was a recognised meeting place for the local
settlers. Mrs Harry Lee would usually make everyone a cup
of tea, and they'd sit around and have a bit of a chat. After

Dad had collected his mail he asked Harry and Jack Lee if they would hire him a horse and cart so he could keep the water supply up. Well, they fixed Dad up with a horse and cart all right, also a fifty-gallon tank, but made it clear that it was a *loan* — that was the way of most people of the area in those days.

By the time he got back we'd put the tents up close to the home site, made a bush shed with an iron roof and built an open fireplace for Mum to cook on. In fact, we'd made ourselves very comfortable, despite the rough conditions. Mum must have been a wonderful sort of woman, coming straight from a nice well-laid-out old English farmhouse kitchen and coping with these primitive conditions. What's more, she came up with a good meal every time. The only thing she had in her favour was that we were always hungry.

The West Australian government had established the Agricultural Bank to help new settlers get on their feet. It wasn't a trading bank, but was used to make loans to settlers for clearing, fencing, dam sinking and purchasing stock and machinery. Dad was granted a clearing loan for 150 acres at twenty-five shillings an acre, paid out on the basis of fifteen shillings to cut down and ten shillings to clear ready for the plough. The bank's inspectors would call, usually monthly, and make payments as the work progressed. This scheme put many settlers on the road to prosperity.

The first inspector I remember was Charlie Mitchell. He was a bonzer bloke and one of the best bushmen in the Narrogin district. He always travelled around in a buggy and pair, and never went anywhere without his Kalgoorlie stretcher — a light, sturdy, but very comfortable portable bed. He'd set it up beside his buggy every night and sleep under the stars — his "Star Hotel". I remember him telling Dad one morning at breakfast how he'd been woken up in the very early hours by what he thought was an earthquake — his bed was rocking violently. "I was awake and up in a flash," he said, "and cripes, wasn't I pleased to see it was only one of your pigs scratching itself on the corner of my stretcher."

To clear the virgin land of green timber was a long, hard and tedious job, with many pitfalls for the "new chum" settler. The usual routine was to "scarf" and burn the big trees on about ten acres, then cut down the bush undergrowth around them before they fell – it was almost impossible to cut bushes in between fallen tree branches. The proper way to scarf a tree was to cut a notch through the outer white sapwood at ground level, right into the dark heartwood. The idea was to start a fire in the heartwood, which is dry, and the trunk would burn through within a few days.

After cutting the scarf, you got a log about four or five inches in diameter and tapered one end; this was "packed" into the scarf, and the other end laid on the ground. Some kindling was then used to get a fire going between the log and the heartwood. The scarf was always cut to face the direction of the prevailing wind so as to maintain a good draught. After the trees had been packed and lit we'd go around and pack them in at least three times a day, otherwise the fire was likely to go out and need relighting. Dad would go round the fires last thing at night if he wasn't too tired. You had to be on the alert when you were packing, because there was always a danger of trees falling.

One morning after breakfast Dad and Mum had gone off to pack in the fires, leaving us kids at the homestead site, when suddenly we were confronted by a tall black man, almost naked. Boy, were we scared. He came right up and asked us for flour and sugar. Charlie refused to give him any of our precious supplies. The man seemed to get a bit annoyed, and he waved his dillybag about and growled, "Flour, sugar". We were beginning to realise these were the only English words he knew. Perce wasn't afraid at all – he just walked up and called him "Uncle". Charlie pulled Perce away, saying: "Please don't hurt my little brother."

While this was going on, Fred, who was a resourceful kid, crawled out under the back flap of the tent and sped off to alert Mum and Dad. In a few minutes Dad thundered into view and the black man was off like a scalded cat. Dad didn't have a dog's chance of catching him. This incident really frightened us kids, so Dad started taking Charlie and Jack to help him pack in the fires, leaving Mum with us younger ones.

About five or six days later I was sweeping around the tent when the old bloke walked up again. One look frightened the hell out of me and I yelled out to Mum. She came out of the tent and said, "Who are you?" in a very loud voice. He just shook his dillybag and mumbled "Flour, sugar". Mum then told Fred to go and find Dad. I'll never forget what she did next. She walked straight up to him, stamped her foot and said, "How dare you come to our tent like this! [I think she meant nearly naked.] How dare you come at all!" Of course he didn't know what she was talking about, and once again he held out his dillybag and growled, "Flour, sugar". At that moment Dad, Charlie, Jack and Fred crashed into view, and he vanished into the bush. We never saw him again.

Later we were told that he was a harmless old chap who went around all the farms cadging for tucker — they called him Jupiter. Then we were annoyed with ourselves for being afraid of him, and sorry for having knocked the poor old bloke back for a lousy bit of flour and sugar. I bet he reckoned we were a pretty miserable mob.

By now we had found a water soak in a sandy patch of an old gully, only about five hundred yards from our camp. This soak had enough water for Dad to start a garden and also to mix "pug" for the walls of the house. Dad marked out the shape of the house, twenty-four feet by twenty-four then put in four-inch diameter posts as uprights. These were eight feet high and six feet apart. Next he nailed "whipstick" she-oak seedlings horizontally about nine inches apart on both sides of the uprights. This left a middle gap which was filled with pug, made simply by mixing water with dirt. Then the wall was plastered over with pug on both sides so that no sticks showed, making it just over six inches thick.

Before a start was made on the roof work a twelve-foot ladder had to be made. It was pretty cumbersome, but Dad had no trouble handling it. As there were no nails or bolts to work with, all the wall plates, ridge poles and rafters were secured with half-inch dowels. We kids soon became very adept at making these dowels from the she-oak seedlings. The interior walls were made of upright poles two to three inches in diameter, placed close together, set eighteen inches deep into the ground and lined on both sides with whitewashed hessian. The floor, of course, remained as dirt. Jack Lee came along one day as we were building the house, and I can remember him saying to Dad, in his very slow drawl, "When the white ants get into them there walls, down'll come Father, Son and Holy Ghost". Parts of the wall were still standing fifty years later.

When all this was finished Dad put a veranda round the house, which made it a very cool and cosy home to live in. The hole we made digging out the dirt for the pug was made into a cellar. We did this simply by putting poles across it, filling in the gaps with a good layer of tea-tree and covering the lot with dirt, heaping it up in the middle to allow water to run off. We then dug steps down to it and put in a home-made flywire door. We reckoned this was the coolest spot in Western Australia, ideal for setting jellies and blancmange, and also for keeping butter, meat and other perishable food in fresh condition.

As Dad and Mum were very strict Church of England folk, they would not allow any work to be done on Sundays, and every Sunday evening Dad would read from the Bible and we'd sing our favourite hymns together. Our Sunday evening sing-song soon became known around the district, and on some nights we had up to ten neighbours turn up to join in with us. These people were not all of the same religion, so Dad never preached. He just read a short lesson from the Bible, then different ones would choose hymns for us to sing.

Dad was very experienced in all aspects of farming, especially haystack building, and he offered to help the Lee brothers in return for their kindness when we had first lobbed into the district. While he was helping the Lees we camped by the large outcrop from which the area got its name. I loved exploring Kirk's Rock; especially I liked flushing the lizards out of their little caves. These iggies, as I called them, were lightning fast, and gave Spring a lot of running practice and me a lot of fun.

Spring was a kangaroo dog we had bought for five pounds.

He was our first roo dog, but in fact by this time we had another one as well, a bitch called Fan. She and Spring hunted
well together, and we hoped later to have pups to sell. Roo
dogs were in great demand, and pricey – five pounds was a
lot of money in those days.

The Lee brothers were well established, with a good solid
house, a freshwater well, good fencing, good horses and a
good flock of sheep. Only Harry Lee was married, and he and
Mrs Lee had one daughter, Mavis. Mum and Mrs Lee had become great friends, Dad got on well with Harry and Jack, and
we kids hit it off with everyone, so all was well with the
world.

The Saturday before Christmas 1909 the Lees lent Dad a
horse and cart to take us four boys to a Christmas tree party
at the White Well hall, four miles west of Wickepin on the
Narrogin Road. There were a lot of kids there, including
three Faceys. Ike and Joe were all right, but Albert was a
grumpy kid who swore and called us "bloody new chums".
He was just over school age and so didn't get a present;
maybe that was why he was so grumpy. My present was a
book called *What Katy Did*. I forget now what it was all
about, but I do remember that the first words were "Katy's
name was Katy Carr". Although it was really a children's
party, the older folk took over later in the evening and danced
till dawn.

While up at Lees' we boys used to go trapping possums.
This was something we'd been doing for a while on our own
property. The dried skins were worth seven shillings and sixpence a pound, while roo skins were five shillings a pound.
Overall, skins brought us in about two pounds per week –
not bad money in those days.

There was much more to trapping possums than just nail-
ing a noose on a tree and hoping for the best. Firstly the
snares had to be properly made – from about two feet of Russian hemp string fortified with very fine tie-wire, much the
same as was used for rabbits. You then had to find where the
possums lived. Their favourite trees were old white gums
(wandoo) with a bit of a lean and a good few hollows in the

branches. You could generally pick the inhabited trees by fresh scratch marks on the bark.

Having satisfied yourself where the possums were, you cut a seven or eight feet post about two and a half inches to three inches thick, leant it against the tree, and set the snare a little above half-way down. It's natural for possums to take the easiest way down when they leave their hollow, so they'll use your leaning post to descend by, and hopefully walk straight into your snare. Of course it didn't always happen that way, but at least it helped you to catch a lot.

After catching your possum, you had to be very careful not to cut the skin and to keep it as square as possible; also you had to be sure you pegged it out to dry on the south side of the tree, away from direct sunshine. The buyers were pretty fussy: they'd reject any skins that were badly shaped, cut or sunshrivelled, or at any rate pay you much less for them. The best time to set the snares was just before sundown, and you collected the catch early next morning, before sun-up if possible — otherwise the dingos would beat you to it and maul them. I can tell you it wasn't all beer and skittles trapping possums in those days.

Dad stayed with the Lees till their harvest was finished; then we all returned to our own block.

When we got back from Kirk's Rock it was the middle of the non-burning season, so we could only do odd jobs around the farm. Burning was banned from November 15th till February 15th. Dad put a six feet netting fence around the house to keep the chooks out, and we boys continued to collect possum and roo skins. By now we'd become pretty shrewd hunters. We'd nutted out all the possums' favourite trees within half a mile of our house and knew exactly where to find the biggest and best mobs of grey kangaroos. You needed to know a few locations because you had to approach roos against the wind.

On some evenings Dad would shoulder his double-barrelled shotgun and take us boys bird-shooting with him. His main game now were bronze-winged pigeons — they were much better eating than parrots, and were sitting shots when they came to the soak for a drink around sundown. On a few occasions he was lucky enough to bag a bustard — we used to call them wild turkeys. These birds were delicious eating but very scarce. Of course all native birds, and animals, are protected by law now.

When the burning season opened, Dad set fire to the fifty-odd acres he had burned and chopped down the previous year. It wasn't a very good burn, so we all hopped in to clear it up ready for the plough. Dad wanted to put in a few acres of wheat for our seed the next year.

Since we'd moved into our house, with its nice kitchen and brand new Metters No. 2 stove, Mum was the happiest woman in Western Australia. She had a fenced-in vegetable garden down by the soak, and chooks ran free around the whole area. We'd also fenced a ten acre paddock below the house, which included the soak, mainly for our cow, Beauty. She'd wander away if let loose. We also kept a couple of pigs in one corner, well away from the new house of which we were all so proud.

At 3.30 a.m. on April 10th 1910, I remember Dad carrying me out on his shoulders to see Halley's Comet. It was then at its best viewing stage, slightly to the south-east. Dad said to me, "Take a good look at it youngster: you've got a good chance of seeing it again". I did.

During the following month, Ted Heheir put in twenty acres of wheat for us on a half-share basis. He was a neighbour of ours. Dad supplied the land, seed and super and Ted did all the work. Later the same year Dad got an Agricultural Bank loan to sink a dam. We all hopped in and cleared a catchment site, then employed a dam sinker, Peter Spurr from Jitarning. It was hard going all the way, but he did a good job and it held water like a bottle.

By Christmas we had everything going for us. Dad had cleared 150 acres ready to put in a crop. He'd put in for a horse loan from the Ag. Bank and everything seemed to be plain sailing. He let us have a lazy time over Christmas and New Year, but had us going again on January 2nd doing the odd jobs we'd put off during the Christmas spell. Not long after this, Ted Heheir came along with stripper and winnower to harvest the wheat he'd put in. It yielded eighty bags. Our share of forty bags was just sufficient seed for Dad's 1911 cropping programme.

Our first job in 1911 was to fence in the twenty acres of stubble to give us a good paddock of feed for when the horses arrived. We were pretty lucky getting a good summer thunderstorm that year. It nearly filled our dam, giving us boys a damn good swimming pool and plenty of water for the horses (when we got them) and other stock. Up till this time we'd relied on the soak water for our cow, pigs and chooks. We were also very lucky in having a thousand gallon tank full of rainwater at the house. Dad and we lads now began building a stable and yards for the horses. The chaff-house and grain shed would be under the same roof as the stables, which would make feeding the horses a much easier job.

Mum was expecting her eighth baby about the end of February, so she made arrangements to stay with some friends in Cottesloe. On the day Mum was due to leave, Mrs Lee drove down in her buggy early in the morning to take her into Wickepin in time to catch the train. I bet Mum wasn't looking forward to that trip at all. Leave home 8 a.m., twenty mile drive over very rough track to Wickepin, take train to Narrogin, wait for Albany Express and arrive Perth 10 a.m. the next day; then local train to Cottesloe. About twenty-seven hours' travelling time all together. Charlie did his best to take Mum's place with the cooking and looking after Perce and Hilda; Jack, Fred and I could look after ourselves pretty well. And I must say Charlie did a good job.

On March 2nd our Sandgroper brother was born, and named Hubert David Miller. Because he was born in our new country we kids immediately dubbed him the Aussie P'fella, and the nickname Fella stuck to him all his life. There was great joy and gladness in the camp when Mum returned with our lovely baby brother, and it was a day or two before we settled down and things got into full swing again.

The loan for horses and harness was approved, and Dad had ordered winkers, reins, collars, hames and plough chains. The swingletrees for a four-horse team he made himself out of bush timber. Matt Bodey of Pingelly was to deliver four good farm horses to our place early in May.

We were all eagerly waiting to start putting in our first wheat crop, and every detail had been planned for the big occasion. Harry Lee had carted out four tons of superphosphate that Dad had ordered through Jack Adams of Wickepin, and it was stacked in the new shed with the forty bags of seed wheat. We had the loan of a three-furrow stump plough and a thirteen-disc seed drill from our next-door neighbours Bill and Bob Rousette. It now only needed the arrival of the horses for us to get cracking. But it was not to be.

On the morning of April 29th Dad didn't feel well, so he spent the day in bed. As far as I can recollect, this was the first day's work he'd ever missed. Next morning he felt better and reckoned he had a bit of a cold that he'd soon work off, but Mum talked him into staying in bed for another day to make sure. He got up on the third day. It was pretty windy and cold, so he stayed inside in front of a nice warm fire. He seemed in good spirits, ate a light meal in the evening, and went to bed as usual. None of us boys, and I'm sure Mum and probably Dad himself, knew how seriously ill he was. During the night he had a relapse and became delirious. Mum managed to calm him down, and he went into a deep sleep. He never woke up. It was about 10 a.m. the next day, May 2nd 1911, that he died.

I'll never forget Mum calling us four boys into the bedroom and saying quietly "Your father's dead". We looked at each other dumbstruck for a while, then burst into tears. Mum cried too, but she was the first to control herself and do what had to be done. What a position to be in – no transport, nearest doctor in Narrogin forty-five miles away, nearest police in Wickepin, twenty-two miles. Mum sent Charlie and Jack to our nearest neighbour, Mr Hickenbotham – we called him Mr Hicks for short. Mr Hicks had no transport either, so they walked up to Kirk's Rock to tell the Lee brothers, who got word through to Wickepin.

After Charlie and Jack left, Fred and I milked the cow and did the separating. By now Mum had dressed Hilda and

Perce and had fed Fella, so we made her a cup of tea. Mum looked really awful, and Fred and I were terrified she might die too. I can tell you we were very pleased when Charlie, Jack and Mr Hicks got back about 3.30. Soon we had some sandwiches and a pot of tea going, and Mum came out and talked with Mr Hicks. He was a good chap, and we were glad when he offered to stay the night to keep us company.

Charlie and Mr Hicks were up first thing in the morning and got breakfast for all of us. When Mum came out of her bedroom my heart sank. She looked even worse, really ill. I doubt anyone could imagine the agony of mind, body and soul she went through that night to prompt her to write this:

> All through the night, the spirit crushed remained,
> In stupor sunk, bereft of power of feeling.
> E'en sorrowing tears, that could not be restrained,
> Too deep alas the anguish for their healing.

The next day a policeman and a doctor came, and they took Dad's body back to Wickepin. Before they left, the doctor put Mum's mind at rest by telling her a post-mortem wouldn't be required. Mrs Lee came along and took Mum, Hilda, Perce and Fella to her parents' farm, five miles north of Wickepin. Mr Hicks stayed with the rest of us. Everyone did all they could to help.

Dad was buried in the Wickepin cemetery on May 5th. The Lee brothers had lent Mr Hicks a horse and cart to take us boys to the funeral, and Mrs Lee took care of Mum and the three children. After the funeral, Charlie, Jack, Fred, Mr Hicks and I ate the few sandwiches we'd brought with us, had a drink from the waterbag and camped the night in the cart. We went home the next day and Mrs Lee brought Mum back on the 7th. After Mrs Lee left we were alone in what now seemed to us a hostile and forbidding great Australian bush.

I've often thought since what an awful few weeks that must have been for Mum, stuck out there in the never never with seven children under the age of 14, three of them needing constant care and attention. Having no transport was an added worry, but luckily none of us met with an accident during that time. I remember Mum saying afterwards it wasn't too bad during the day when she had us kids to talk to, but at night when we were all asleep, and that "deathly bush silence" settled in, life became almost unbearable – so much so, she said, that once or twice the idea of suicide occured to her as the easiest way out. Luckily, the thought of leaving us alone in the world, and her absolute faith in God, quickly put those ideas out of her mind.

Mum coped with all the work single-handed and still found time to comfort us and make sure we never missed a meal, helping us with odd jobs during the day, and every evening joining us together in prayer and Bible reading. Never once during that dreadful time did Mum's faith really falter, believing so implicitly as she did that God's will was always for the best.

I never told Mum then, nor did I later, that after Dad's death I stopped believing in her God. I could never believe that taking Dad to heaven, as Mum said God did, was for the best for any of us. And then praying to Him for help, when it was *He* that caused the tragedy, was too silly for words. That's what I thought at the time, and still do. Yet it gave Mum the courage and strength to carry on.

Living out in the solitude of the bush brings one very close to nature, and you soon realise beyond doubt that nobody and no being on earth or in heaven could alter the course of nature – could stop a river flowing, the wind blowing, a flower blooming, or even a bird building its nest in the right season. Everything that happens in this world happens naturally; therefore the ruling system of the university is nature. So I consider myself a "naturist" (yes, I know that word has another meaning but I'm hoping I won't be misunderstood). Throughout my life I've only ever relied on nature to provide all my worldly needs – and to be dinkum I've not done too bad.

About three weeks after Dad's funeral we all went to Wickepin to live, taking with us our only substantial possession, Beauty the cow. During those three weeks Mrs Lee did not stay idle: without letting us know, she started a collection from folks around the Kirk's Rock district to raise money to help us settle in Wickepin. She only had three mail days in which to collect from the local farmers, but we were told afterwards that that good lady bailed up everyone who went past her house and asked them to subscribe. Through her efforts, Mrs Lee was able to hand over to Mum more than ninety pounds. Those early settlers were really kind and generous.

A Country Childhood

Roger McDonald

Bribbaree had steely-grey ironbarks along a dry creekbed, cypress pines in wheatfields, a handful of weatherboard houses set back from dusty tracks. Horsedrawn wagons and high-cabbed trucks brought wheat sacks to the silos. Along corrugated dirt roads trees met overhead, making a tunnel where car headlights were continually swallowed up. The local police sergeant made his rounds on horseback. There was a bush nurse instead of a doctor. On odd days, my father lifted me to watch blitz wagons roaring through in the middle distance — army convoys bowling along through high grass. Trucks without drivers, I thought.

Bribbaree had existed only since 1917, when the Forbes-Stockinbingal railway line went through. During the 1939-45 war, people drove sulkies to church, tethering horses to brick and iron spike fences in the bush. The wheat silos of the district were like giants' castles in a story book. The names of places where my father went preaching on Sundays rang like bells: Thuddungra, Quandialla, Tubbul, Bimbi, Morangarell. They were legendary places rising from the grass, appearing over the rim of a windshield.

In the manse backyard was an earth dunny. My brother Don dropped my rabbit slippers down there. My mother fished them out with a sapling. I was unable to love those slippers any more, but had to wear them. Don dippered creamy house paint on to my head — giving me a shampoo, rubbing in handfuls of sawdust to make foam. Don was inventive, resourceful, thorough and definite in everything he did. Not like me at all. I see myself standing dreamily still, only half aware of what was being done to me.

A woolly blanket on the splintery-boarded verandah; dry summer grasses taller than a forest; a bumping dangerous ride in a stroller to the bakery. At the bush nurse's, Don had a boil lanced and the sister screamed recriminations at him as the pus squirted on to her starched white uniform. I alone believed that her accusations were not an injustice. I knew that Don could do anything, even aim his boils.

Church was a place to lie on the floor and look up at the ceiling through monotonous, wheezy hymns and earnest prayers for those in danger on foreign soil. I twisted a piece of smooth cotton handkerchief around my thumb, stroked my index finger over it, and "smoodged". To keep out the sun's glare the church windows were whitewashed in a pattern of curly waves, leaving the imprint of muslin. Continual staring threw endless pictures on the glass.

While my father stood at his lectern doing his job, explaining Christianity, drawing his congregation's attention to the original meaning of Greek and Hebrew words, I had no special thoughts about him, he was just Dad. This was what he did on Sundays, three or even four times through the day, north to Quandialla, south to Tubbul. In later years (in Temora and Bourke) I developed the feeling that whereas other dignitaries like the doctor, the bank manager, the solicitor, and even the headmaster had something solid to hand over in return for whatever was asked of them, my father's offering was sealed behind a wall of purposeful, carefully thought-out, but truly incomprehensible language. I liked his children's addresses best. They were short, low-vocabulary sermons followed by the children's hymn, a jaunty "Jesus Loves Me" or "Jesus Wants Me for a Sunbeam". Then the children were allowed to file out and play among the parked cars, horses, gravestones, tree thickets of the churchyard while adults stayed behind for the main sermon. We climbed the trees that groaned against the corrugated iron roof, and looked down through scratch marks on the whitewashed windows on to ladies' hats and bald bowed heads.

In 1944 we moved to Temora, not long before the Japanese breakout at Cowra, one hundred miles away. My mother locked doors, barred windows, and kept a copperstick handy until the last escapee was rounded up. I did not know about this at the time. Because of its remoteness the war made me feel safe. My greatest fear was lightning. I sat on the verandah with my parents, watching a distant thunderstorm, asking if it was close or far away. *How* far away? Where the soldiers were fighting?

When I was satisfied that it was as far away as where the soldiers were fighting, I felt secure.

I started school at Temora, walking down a long sweeping road from the hillside where the large, brick-built, ferociously cold, verandah-tiled Federation manse was located. Down I went into the terrors of the town. I was too young for what was asked of me, only four and a half, still wrapped in my cocoon. I developed stomach pains. Two brothers named Schick hid behind fences and leapt out whenever they had the opportunity, throwing punches. They were aged only six or seven, but were as fearsome as grown men. It was a daily nightmare getting past them until a neighbour, Mr Rogers, followed behind in his small two-seater car, sprang out, jammed the bullies into the dicky-seat in the back where they wet their pants, and delivered them to the headmaster.

Even so, I kept taking roundabout routes home, avoiding lesser bullies, Catholics, savage dogs, over-friendly strangers. To calm my stomach I wedged myself over the seats of chairs, groaning in relief. Strain was the word used then instead of stress for the condition I was in. The cure was to "be a soldier".

Directly behind the manse, wheatfields began. At harvest time a horsedrawn reaper-binder was used: rabbits, hares and rats scattered everywhere. Stooks were built, and a huge, boxlike, belt- and cog-festooned thresher arrived. The stooks made ideal cubby-houses until they were fed into the mouth of the thresher. Then the harvest was over and life was empty and unexciting until Don found a box of wax matches and burnt down the Rogers' haystack. The smoke filled the sky over the town and there were terrible recriminations that died down into general agreement that innocence was responsible. I knew better. It was impossible for me to believe that Don did not know what he was doing.

On one side of the house a clump of gum trees was left standing from when the paddocks were cleared. Tree climbing was the thing I loved best, getting up high to watch the Tiger Moths that continually hiccoughed and plunged over the town, leftovers from the wartime training airport. One day I fought with my best friend, Peter James, over who was the best tree climber. We punched and kicked until my mother separated us, ordering us to shake hands. Peter James advanced on me with a grin and without warning punched me in the guts, then ran away. (Later he became Temora's mayor.)

I was a weedy, skeletonised child. Old ladies liked my sad possum eyes, but called me a Belsen horror, and asked my mother if she thought I would survive. Despite this I was never sick. Don was. He had diptheria and asthma and once, on holidays at Tumut, was whipped into the current of the river and swept downstream, almost drowning. Pure luck shot him back on to a shingly bend. When he recovered he offered me a Hitler Jump, which I willingly accepted. Hitler Jumps were a trick of my father's. You bent over, put your hands between your legs, and were whizzed through a somersault in a perfect arc, landing square on your feet. Don lined me up on a hard, cement-built Tumut vernadah. Over I went and landed on my chin, blood everywhere. The scar where I was stitched together still feels tender.

Back home, Don and the James boys suggested I rattle a stick in the limb-hollow of a tree and see what happened. I agreed. They ran off. A swarm of bees came out, stinging my face and arms. I was due to go with my father on an overnight trip to Wagga, and I went, after much debate, sobbing and swollen, clutching a lump of Reckitt's Blue in a clean rag to dab on the stings as Dad steered the Chev sedately through the countryside, asking me to hold the wheel steady while he rolled his cigarettes.

Because I looked amazingly young for my age I was chosen to play a kindergarten child in a street parade celebrating an important anniversary in New South Wales Education. I had to sit on the back of a truck, building with wooden blocks and counting with an abacus. It was the proudest moment of my life, waving to strangers and being admired for something I wasn't. I could not seem to earn any sort of praise by being myself. I could never run or fight, and could not master arithmetic. I was not religious, but had developed a truly Presbyterian psyche, absorbing the message that it was "not what one said, but what one did, that counted". This way I learnt to discount my own wishes, as fatal a streak as arrogance.

Dad built a balsawood plane for me, a glider with intricate struts, papered over with tissue. I felt excluded from the preoccupation that went into its making, but was excited by the idea of flight. Each night the glider was put away in a cupboard, to keep my hands off it. But it was Dad who did the damage. While preparing a sermon he accidentally dumped a copy of Cruden's *Concordance* on the fuselage, crushing it to bits. Another plane was promised, but I knew it would never get made. I did not want it made. I would not be the cause of putting my father through another such effort of dedication. It was not like him. It was not like me. I was embarrassed. When I turned seven my mother went to enormous trouble to give me my first proper birthday party with all my classmates attending, and the process traumatised me. I never wanted to feel so special again. Not this way. Not from outside my self. What had I done to deserve it? A number had flipped over on a calendar. That was all. It was a relief when everyone went home and I could isolate myself in reading.

For my book-present my parents had given me *Little Round Stairway* by Gladys Lister. It was the story of a girl named Piettra who was brought up by gypsies when her family home was destroyed in a bushfire and she was orphaned. After wandering with Piettra in their care for some time the gypsies returned to the house site where only a brick chimney was left standing. Piettra, who hated sleeping in a bed with a tangle of gypsy children, persuaded the Gypsy Father to set up a curtain-flap and camp bed in the chimneyplace. There she lived while practising tightrope walking in the gypsy circus.

I still have this book. When I look at the picture of Piettra's burnt-out chimney in *Little Round Stairway* I feel what I felt at seven, a sickening fascination. I smell the cold ashes and rub the rotting mortar of the bricks between my fingertips, and hear the wind tossing the gums behind the place where the family once lived. I want to be there. On the ground against the chimney wall is an abandoned teapot. The drawing of the shadowed camp stretcher and the exposed flaking brickwork of the lonely chimney is crude and haunting. Other pictures in *Little Round Stairway* are smoothly idealised. This one looks truthful. Something spoke to me through the image of destruction and rehabitation. I liked the idea of playing somewhere like that with a pretty girl. I envied the intense privacy of Piettra's hideaway and her public appearances in the circus. But way past these consolations was the absoluteness of the burnt-out chimneyplace. It was beyond strain. It was what would be left when the busy, demanding making of the world was done. I sank down into it. It was mine.

One day in 1949 (the year I turned eight) portable amplifiers were brought into the school playground. We were all lined up, then brought forward in a tight cluster. For once, nobody spoke. It was the same at the convent school next door. A nation of school children waited breathlessly while the prime minister, Mr Chifley, announced he was letting off an explosive charge to mark the start of the Snowy Mountains Scheme. We imagined him lighting a wick or pushing a plunger. The speakers shook with a distant, blurred vibration and the ground seemed to tremble. Motorised equipment started up, bulldozers and graders smashed trees and tossed aside rocks in our imaginations. We cheered till we went hoarse. We glimpsed the future. It would be like a giant game of cars. The purpose in becoming a grown-up became clear. We would turn into truck drivers, engine drivers, heavy plant operators. In my case I would become an aeroplane pilot.

Sometimes on Mondays (my father's day off) we were collected from school early. Out we went past the boundary of the town into a different world and found a dam or a creekbed for yabbying. In the holidays we stayed on farms. The Cooks at Thuddungra put Don on a horse and started for him a future of horsebreaking, leatherwork, mustering and buckjumping that took a dent years later, out on the Paroo, when he damaged his back in a rodeo event. Now he's a farmer in New Zealand. Gavin, aged five, clutched the steering wheel of a little grey Fergie and wanted nothing else. Now he farms south of Charters Towers, riding a gigantic Phillips tractor through the night all lit up like the spaceship Enterprise. I loved being on a farm too. I had nothing to do, no responsibilities, no strains. I mooned about reading books, steered a sulky down to the mailbox, floated on my back in the dam avoiding leeches. Mrs Cook made memorable Easter eggs, pure chocolate all through, hefty as stones. I could stay up late or sleep in. Watching the sun sink over the stubble and the stars come out, and hearing the crickety stillness in the middle of the night broken by a plover's cry or a rabbit's scream as a fox attacked was to experience equilibrium.

We moved to Bourke in 1950. This was not like living in the country at all. It was somewhere else. Bourke was the remotest town in New South Wales, the end of the western line. It was Out West. It was where drunks from Belmore Park opposite Central Station rode up on the Bourke Mail in winter and got straight back on to the slops again. At night they rattled our front gate. They slept on the church porch. They sang in the middle of empty streets at midnight. Others arrived from out of the heat haze of outback stations to blow their cheques – except it was not called the outback then (outback, by definition, being an abstraction, always farther out). During their drying out, they did gardening for housewives, my mother included. Hacking up their lungs over a fork or a spade, digging deep into their pockets, they handed me florins – they must have been rich – and asked me to run messages to the corner store for a pair of bootlaces, a packet of Tally Ho's, a half-dozen Bex, and keep the change.

It was land rather than countryside at Bourke, and out on the edge of town, after cresting the levee banks and looking out across the black-soil plains, there was nothing inviting for the newcomer to step across into. At my feet was a treeless, lumpy, hard, cracked, cattle-pugged ground covered in burr and thistle. In one direction lay the railway line and the meatworks. The other way was the town common, where the blacks lived in shacks made from battered kerosene tins. At their back was the Darling River, a fringe of redgums and coolabahs lining a deep, curry-coloured trench slowly filling with a record-breaking flood on its way down from Queensland. The water came slowly, inexorably. Two months after we arrived the town was surrounded. Blitz wagons with loud-speakers mounted on their roofs drove round at night calling for volunteers to mend ruptured levees. My father and the Catholic priest grew blisters together. All roads were cut, al-though the train still got through from Nyngan and the airport at North Bourke was serviced by army ducks bringing in medical supplies landed by DC-3s. Bourke was a name in the news. Movietone film was shot there. When the water went down it left a rotting-fish, dead-mud smell over the town, and a boy from Sunday School died and was buried by my father in the boggy cemetery in a sky-blue coffin.

At school my brothers and I were among the few who wore shoes. We also wore socks. Out of sight of the house we shoved them down around our ankles, hoping no one would notice the silver-white hairs on our legs sticking out. At the urinal in the boys' toilet the little flap my mother had sewn into my shorts instead of fly-buttons was an object of curios-ity, not mockery. Despite the rock-bottom toughness of Bourke Public School I was not teased or bullied there, as had happened at Temora and later at Scots in Sydney, where sneering was an art form. Monday mornings in the play-ground at Bourke was when Aboriginal kids repeated slabs of dialogue from Friday and Saturday night movies, reacting to the nuance like connoisseurs, gathering big appreciative au-diences around them for Red Skelton and Three Stooges im-itations, doing Gary Cooper parts to the letter, curling the lip, going for the gun. Inside the classroom at Composition and Spelling they had nothing to say. During the shearing season they would disappear for months at a time, doing picking up work in the sheds. And then, if they came back at all, they left school early.

Among Bourke's churchmen there was a demarcated atti-tude towards Aborigines. They were seen as nominally Cath-olic so the Protestants left them alone. My father preached to townsfolk and pastoralists. There was only an evangelist and his son who had the stomach to stay down on the common, as if fellow humans might live there. But evangelists had their bromides too. What the Aborigines themselves wanted was a

question left unasked. They were seen to want filth, ignorance, hopelessness – things nobody else could tolerate.
There was never a people more bucketed with blame.

Before we left Bourke for Sydney when I was twelve my
father and I had our last-ever Shiralee moment together away
out beyond Hungerford somewhere, where he went visiting
station properties in a wide week-long arc. It was red sandy
inland country, beautiful after Bourke. Leopardwood, wilga
and she-oak stretched in every direction like natural park-
land. We nosed in to the side of a lonely track and unpacked
our gear. Soon there was a fire of hot red gidgee logs going,
and the billy had boiled. Dad sipped his tea while I explored.
I climbed to the top of a sandhill where Sturt's desert pea sent
out scarlet runners. A big red kangaroo loped past. I came
back and ate my Camp Pie with bread and butter. When the
stars were out I climbed on to the back seat of the car and covered myself with army blankets against the night chill. Dad
slept on a camp stretcher in the open. I could see the stars
inching around the sky like the hands of a clock. I would have
been happy to come back to somewhere like this every night
of my life.

The First House

Dorothy Hewett

The first house sits in the hollow of the heart, it will never go away. It is the house of childhood become myth, inhabited by characters larger than life whose murmured conversations whisper and tug at the mind. Enchanted birds and animals out of a private ark sail out on tides of sleep, howling, whistling, mewing, neighing, mooing, baaing, barking, to an endless shimmer of wheat and cracked creekbeds. Through the iron gate on the edge of Day's paddock we enter the farm, and drive past the giant she-oak split in two by a strike of lightning. The house lies in the bend of two creeks. The sheepdogs are barking from the verandahs. Beyond is the stable yard with the well in the centre where you let down the bucket to bring up fresh clear water. Large animals move there, draughthouses big as the Spanish Armada champing forever at mangers full of oats, licking at rock salt, or rolling ridiculously in grey sand, hoofs waving in air. Liquid or wild-eyed, the cows file into the cow bails with curled horns and names like Strawberry, Buttercup and Daisy. The sheep jostle together in the pens, the kelpie running and snapping across their backs. The sun reflects off the corrugated iron of the shearing shed till it tilts and topples, crazy as a glasshouse. In the chaffhouse it makes eyes that glitter and run like mice across the floor.

The haystacks prickle and gleam behind the "chunk chunk chunk" of the chaffcutter feeding an endless belt through cogs and wheels. Magpies are sitting carolling on the York gums. At the back of the stable yard is an old, half-rotted horse race where Yarriman, the Aboriginal horse-breaker, drove the wild horses down from the low hills before we were born. To the right of the path through the house paddock where our father staggered with a bloody eye kicked in by Jack, the rogue horse, there is the married couple's flat-fronted, flat-roofed weatherboard humpie, with one door and two eyes for windows like a child's drawing. The red-headed Pommy, Mrs Rogers, is running in and out of the house like a weather woman bringing her underclothes in off the line so that my father won't see them; inside Peggy Rogers is eating her peas off her knife, because "the fork might prick me tongue". Outside in the yard their electric-blue Tin Lizzie is parked waiting to carry them away for ever.

Near the high wire stable gate are the murderous gallows, dripping blood and fat; where the sheep hang with their throats cut. On the other side of the gate is the blacksmith's shop with the grinder and the forge and the black anvil shooting sparks, the floor littered with curls of wood shavings. We hang them over our ears like Mary Pickford. On the left is the ant-heap tennis court where I tried to jump the tennis net and broke my arm and had to be driven fourteen miles over bush roads to the local doctor, with a deal splint my father cut from the wood heap bound round my elbow. My mother sits on the sidelines barracking "good shot" and "butterfingers". Past the tennis court is a dry abandoned dam full of rusty tins where Nancy the black-and-white cow fell in and had to be hauled out, mad-eyed and lowing, with ropes and a pulley.

The little gate opens into the garden with the pink Dorothy Perkins rose climbing on the wire fence, the Geraldton wax bush blooming. The house is ringed with almond and fig trees. In spring the almond blossom falls in white bruised drips on the couch-grass lawn. In summer the twenty-eight parrots crack nuts over our heads till our father goes for the shotgun. At Christmas time we sit on the verandah preparing the nuts for the cake with a silver nutcracker. The twenty-eight parrots flash green and black as they fly away, the nutcracker flashes silver in the sun. We carry the almonds into the kitchen, plunge them in boiling water and peel off the skins, till they curl like brown tissue paper and the almonds emerge smooth and creamy white.

The fig leaves are rough like cows' tongues and the fig skins tingle and burn in our mouths. At night time our father carries us shoulder high to the outside dunny singing "When the moon shines over the cow shed" and "There's a little black cupid in the moon."

The house is built with two wings, the old house and the new. The old house has two corrugated-iron rooms. In the ramshackle sleepout, my grandparents live in an old iron bedstead with silver balls for decoration. The shelves are made of butterboxes filled with paperbacks, and copies of *Bleak House* and *Little Dorrit*, with the ominous Phiz drawings. The Swiss Family Robinson built their treehouse, menaced by giant snakes and jungle. My grandmother's tin trunks are crammed with eyelet-embroidered petticoats with yards of handmade lace, pale leather button-up boots, pearl-buttoned kid gloves and VAD nurses' uniforms from the First World War.

Beside the old sleepout is the little back verandah where the quinces and Jonathan apples are stored to ripen on open wooden shelves. I hide there reading *All Quiet on the Western Front*, and a paperback stolen out of the butterboxes with a cover drawing of a droopy, yellow-haired girl playing the piano, mooned over by a handsome Catholic priest.

Go through the French doors, pleated and dark with dusty muslin curtains, into the enchanted centre, the playroom, the children's domain packed with forty-three dolls and a huge box full of *Alice in Wonderland, Tom the Water Baby, Treasure Island, Wind in the Willows, Peter Pan, Emily of New Moon, A Child's Garden of Verses,* Ida Rentoul Outhwaite's *Elves and Fairies.* Andersen's and Grimm's *Fairy Tales, a Child's History of England, What Katy Did* and *What Katy Did at School, Seven Little Australians, Norah of Billabong, Dot and the Kangaroo, Pollyanna, Daddy Long Legs, Anne of Green Gables, The Tales of Pooh, Robin Hood, Robinson Crusoe, Gulliver's Travels, The Arabian Nights, Little Women* and *Good Wives, Coral Island* and *Tom Brown's School Days, Lamb's Tales from Shakespeare* and all my mother's English *Schoolgirl Annuals.*

The dolls are made of rag, celluloid and china. The china dolls' eyes fall in and rattle about in their heads. On the rag dolls' plaster faces the painted eyes run blue when they are left out in the rain. A black mechanical toy car called Leaping

Lena bucks across the playroom floor. There is a train set with tangled rails, a double-storeyed, butterbox doll's house with wicker furniture and a magic lantern, its wavering images clicking on and off across the wall.

Here is the open whitewashed fireplace where our father roasts potatoes in their jackets under the coals in winter, and in summer piles up gum branches to break the fall of Father Christmas as he tumbles down the chimney. We put out a bottle of beer and a piece of Christmas cake, iced and decorated with silver cashews, to reward him for his trouble.

In summer we sleep in the big sleepout completely enclosed in flywire so that at night we feel as if we are floating in air above the garden and the quiet orchard, borne away by the call of the mopokes. In the morning we wake to a wash of light, a magpie perched on the clothes prop, a rooster crowing from the chook yard at the bottom of the garden. In the dim light we watch the cured hams swaying from the iron hooks above our heads.

An old weatherboard verandah runs right through the centre of the house where the sheep carcasses hang in blood-spotted calico. A big waterbag with a long spout swings by the tankstand, the rainwater tasting of wet hessian. The bathroom has a claw-footed enamel bath and a chip heater, where our mother develops her sepia photographs in an enamel dish on the marble washstand.

The new wing of weatherboard and fibro was built when I was five. There is a big farm kitchen, a black stove with two huge boiling kettles, a long lino-covered pine table, and a jarrah dresser with a recess underneath where we can crawl and hide. Our father sits in the corner, puts the headphones on, and listens to the test cricket on the crystal set.

In the pantry there are sacks of flour, nuts, sugar and potatoes, rows of home-made preserves and jars of jam. The kettles hiss on the blackened stove, the bread rises in the pans set out on the hob, the wheat is ground into meal for our morning porridge, the sheep's head floats in the white basin, muslined from the flies, the cream is slapped into butter between the wooden pats.

The flypaper hangs from the ceiling and catches in our

hair. Blowflies buzz angrily outside the flywire door. Through the kitchen window you can look out on the cannas growing beside the drain, the wattles marking the orchard boundary and the edge of the creek.

In the hall there is an etching of Gladstone, who always chewed every mouthful thirty-six times, and two oil paintings, "The Stag at Bay" by Great-Aunt Eva and "The Deer in the Snow" by Great-Aunt Dora, who died of TB in Woorooloo Sanatorium. Eva's stag has a crooked leg.

The hall is the best place to be when the temperature hits 114 in the shade. We lie on our bellies on the jarrah boards listening to *In a Monastery Garden, Cavalleria Rusticana, Humoresque* and *The Laughing Policeman* on the wind-up His Master's Voice gramophone. Sometimes we play lady wrestlers, or impersonate Two-Ton Tony Galento on the strip of Persian-patterned carpet.

On the other side of the hall is Great-Aunt Eva's bedroom, all polished lino, cheval mirror and oak bedroom suite, reflecting the light. When Aunty Eva comes, once or twice a year, she lies in bed with us, reciting *The Schooner Hesperus, Hiawatha, Horatius at the Bridge* and *Little Jim*, while we pull out her grey hairs one by one.

In the bedroom next door that I share with my mother and sister, I have a little single bed where I lie sweating at night, keeping one eye on the griffins on the wardrobe door, which are likely to metamorphose into real monsters, and the other eye on the square of light from the bedroom window, which is likely to let in all things that go bump in the night. The little oil night-light with its round milky glass floats luminous above the dressing table, where my mother sits singing, "There's a long, long trail awinding into the land of my dreams".

On the right of the hall is the sitting room where we are allowed to go only on special occasions, or when the Salvation Army chaplain calls in overnight. Then my mother plays hymns and makes mistakes on the iron-framed German piano. My grandfather's favourite is "Rock of Ages", my father's is "Abide with Me". There is a leatherette sofa and two armchairs, an oval jarrah table and six high-backed dining chairs. The table is always draped in an orange tasselled cover with a leather centrepiece in a cut-out design of fruit and flowers. On the walls are prints of "The Watcher on the Hill", a group of wild horses with flying manes and rolling eyes, a herd of Highland cattle fording a stream, some Victorian English girls in frilly muslin pinafores toasting chestnuts in front of a fire grate, a sunflower painted on glass, and Great-Aunt Eva's out-of-perspective painting of a huge Newfoundland, paws outstretched under a half-drowned girl, a ship's funnel smoking in the distance.

The fire grate has fleur-de-lys tiles, and elephants from Bombay on the mantelpiece. The bow windows are hung with pale yellow linen curtains bordered with William Morris fruit. They frame the lightning-struck she-oak and the line of salmon gums, shiny and creaking in the wind, their bark hanging in rags like giant beggar women.

Under a broken-backed wattle in the orchard we have our cubby: an old dunny, cement-floored with a row of tulip tiles behind the seat, and a tent made of sewn wheatbags. By the swing is the wrecked Willys-Knight chassis that once belonged to our grandfather. I play *Death and the Maiden* laid out on the cracked leather seat, dressed up in my mother's crepe de Chine wedding dress, pleated from neck to hem, with the remnants of a gossamer train.

The orchard is heavy with peach and apricot, nectarine and mandarin, quince and pear. A silver balloon hangs for a moment on the quince tree and floats away. The grapevines are pendulous with pale green ladies' fingers. The orchard is thick with paddy and pig melons. I suck the transparent globule of gum prised off the jam tree. The moon rests on the stable roof like a great ruby bubble. My mountain pony Silver steps out daintily, pulling up clumps of capeweed, her hoofs curling like Arabian slippers. She has foundered in the wheat.

Every spring the magpies nest in the almond tree, raising naked-necked fledglings, their beaks gaping for worms. The tomtit builds its hanging nest and lays three warm speckled eggs amongst dry grass and feathers. A wagtail balances on the top rail of the wire fence hung with dewdrops, chirping "sweet pretty creature". The drops hang, glisten and slide.

The plover nests in the furrows made by the plough. The quail settles down in the long grass over her eggs. The pee-wits are crying over the wheat. Rain's coming – the black cockatoos sweep down from the rock hill and collect like black rags on the gums. The racehorse goannas are racing through the orchard, switching their tails. A silver-green tree frog leaps into the pink ivy geranium hanging by the tankstand. I am running to the end of the farm. I am running to the end of the rainbow where there is, apparently, a pot of gold. I am holding the silver balloon on the end of a long string. "The crow makes wing to the rooky wood", and Trix, the sixteen-year-old shearers' tabby, sits patiently in the doll's pram under the almond trees, a frilled baby-doll's bonnet tied under her white whiskers.

My grandfather goes out to feed the poddy calves, the milk bucket clanging at his thigh. In the kitchen garden Mr Wrigglesford leans on his spade on the dry manure heap telling me stories of bardies and earthworms and furry black caterpillars. An old mate of my grandfather's, he goes on monthly benders, and swims, making tracks like a goanna, through the dust to his camp on the other side of the machinery shed. One day he will mysteriously disappear, and we will sit mourning over his tent props and his blackened billy on a cold heap of ashes.

In summer the centre of our house shifts from the kitchen to the verandahs. We sit waiting for the Albany Doctor to blow up, rippling the tops of the wattles along the creek, while the voices murmur on and on telling their endless tales of past and present. The trees lift up their roots and come closer to the house to listen. Then legendary characters stalk the Avon Valley, the ghosts of the gold miners on the road to Kalgoorlie with their wheelbarrows, riding, driving their drays, to camp at Split Rock at the bottom of our orchard; Joe Anchor, who lies buried under Joe Anchor's rock at the edge of the farm – was he seaman or drifter?; the Ridleys and Bells and Hothams who take over the country like crows; the Mundy brothers with their bell-bottom trousers swaggering through the towns; the silvertails playing golf and holding cocktail parties, dancing to their doom, while their farms are taken over by the banks and the rabbits.

We lie in the hammock flying out above stars and wind, listening as worlds coalesce, floating us down the avenues of sleep.

The houses of childhood all have this mythical quality lost under the mist of time — the wooden house on the shores of the Swan River and the holiday cottage behind the sand dunes on the beach at King George's Sound. As long as I can remember we have had these holiday places.

Every year in October we go to the Perth Royal Show and stay in my grandfather's jarrah house on the river at Como, where we learn to swim with water wings at the end of a spindly jetty. Globules of jellyfish litter the sand, transparent and quivering. It is the same jetty where my mother went, travelling with her father as a little girl, driving over the causeway in a spanking horse and buggy that left all the other drivers for dead. The air of that house always seems full of the sound of Indian doves cooing. There is a small jarrah forest on the other side of a wooden stile, where we run to catch the tram and ferry to the little city. The rooms are dark and cool, a long living room furnished in oak, a primitive lean-to kitchen, the bedrooms lined, floor to ceiling, with pale green pressed iron. Our water comes from a stone well with a hand pump and a bucket at the back door. We carry fluted pink and white shaded oil lamps from room to room.

At night strange bleeps and muffled screams come from the back bedroom, where an ancient caretaker called Lapp tunes in on his home-built crystal set. We sit with the headphones on for hours trying to decipher something from the rushing airwaves, but we never hear anything that remotely resembles a human voice, or the sound of music. but we are fiercely loyal to the end, and indignant when the grown-ups make fun of Lapp's invention.

There is a copse of wattle between the house and the river. Through the door and across the verandah an old donkey grazes in an empty paddock, like a framed picture. On the other side of the wattle grove lives Mrs Pooley, a tall thin woman with wisps of yellow-white hair, who breeds Pekinese behind a blue convolvulus hedge.

The zamia palms drift their fronded patterns across the white sand.

After the harvest, we travel 250 miles to the South Coast and live for two or three months in a tiny cottage of two rooms and a kitchen beside the sea. The landscape is forbidding and melancholy, with black rocks and low dark scrub lit by the occasional gleam of sunlight on granite or wave or sand dune. The places around us have magical names like Torbay, Nornalup, Nannarup and Two People Bay. Lagoon and ocean, seabird and scrub, lonely and deserted, are surrounded by great karri forests where you can drive a car through a hollow tree. A petrified forest covers the sand dunes. We fish on mirror-smooth rivers. In their green depths white drowned forests drift, quivering. A great kingfish breaks the surface and flashes through sunlight to land jiggling on the end of a line.

At night the lighthouse on Breaksea flicks on and off across the Southern Ocean and steamers with smoking funnels sail by on their way to the ends of the world. The beach on one side is ringed by a scrubby headland like a resting emu, on the other by Bald Head, a sheer crag of black rock. In the distance the tiny island of Dunder Rock glitters in the setting sun. Behind it rises a mountain glimmering like Shangri-la. At Emu Point there is a spring where the Dutch explorers called in to water their ships and Green Island where the colonial ladies fled from a black ambush. The beach is an arc of hard white sand stretching along the way. Cars drive to the point when the tide is out but often, on their way back, they meet their doom. Bogged or caught in the incoming surf, they wash, bobbing ludicrously out to sea. Pacific gulls fly low over the dunes, pods of whales are sometimes beached, dark-humped and dying in the shallows. We gather white crenellated shells and put them to our ears to hear the sea sighing. At night we lie in bed listening to the surf breaking and lulling against the beach. Sometimes the sound is so loud and the house is so small, we feel as if we are rocking on the surface of the sea, going out with the tide.

Next door is a wild tract of reserve covered in eucalyptus and prickly bush twined with purple clematis. We build elaborate cubbies floored with moss and roam with our boy cousins, playing wild horses, Robin Hood and Maid Marian and the Merry Men. Behind the house, on the wet bracken hillsides at Miramar, we go blackberrying and run down the slopes to fling ourselves into the surf, the salt smarting the bramble cuts on our legs and arms. At night our father makes big fires of driftwood in the open fireplace and we sit, flushed and stinging with sunburn, in wicker chairs, playing rummy and Rickety Kate on the round oak table.

At the South Coast, where a honeymoon couple once whirled to their death in the blowhole, the sea rushes in under giant granite causeways, sucking and swirling through gaps and holes. If you lean out over hummocks of rough grass on the headland, you can see Jimmy Newell's Harbour where he took shelter, running in under the knoll from a raging storm. King waves sweep over coastal rocks, drowning intrepid fishermen. At Frenchman's Bay there are the stone remnants of jetties and huts left by the French whalers. The wild sea and historic past seem to merge in one glamorous tale.

At the end of the summer we pack up our shells, call "Steamer, steamer" for the last time, and go back to put them on the farm mantelpiece, listening to the suck of the surf in our faraway inland country.

My grandfather's house on the Swan River disappeared long ago under high-rise apartment blocks. The wooden house by the sea still stands unchanged, silvered with age, but the beachfront is thickly settled and a caravan park cuts off the house from the dunes and the sea. The farm is long since sold and the farmhouse derelict. The new owners have shifted to a kit home beside Rock Hill, away from the creek and closer to the electric-light poles.

Is it still there on the far side of Day's paddock in the bend of three creeks, unchanged, unclaimed except by the weather and the starry wastes of sky? Do the ghostly draughthorses wheel and gallop through the dark? Through the open French doors swinging in the wind is a scratchy 78 still playing the Hallelujah Chorus over and over again . . . Hallelujah, Hallelujah?

The Disappearance of Conlan's Swamp

Sally McInerney

Most parts of our lives seem ordinary as breathing, but that may be only because we are busy living in them at the time. Children especially have no way of judging the relative strangeness of things; some people could have been raised by wolves and still have believed their lives to be ordinary.

I see now that the disappearance of Conlan's Swamp was a rural tragedy.

Conlan must have been a cocky or hayseed farmer who sold up, went to the city or died young: no families in the district wore his name. In that part of the country, names of hills, creeks, and even big rocks jutting from the sides of hills and covered with drought-defying lichen, have men's names attached to them (almost always in the possessive), harking back one hundred and fifty years or so to the time when names gave a recognisable face to the land in the central west. So our farm was still known as Hickey's even though Mr Hickey the schoolmaster was long dead, and the grandchildren of the boys he'd used to clear his land (Geography lessons, he called those axe and shovel days) had children of their own at the same little school, lining up under the kurrajong tree each morning to salute the flag, and trying to learn the polka under the pepper trees, and watching the teacher's cigarette ash burn down until it keeled over on his desk like a grey caterpillar, dead.

As people came and went, wild nature was criss-crossed with paths, and frightened them less. They gave their properties romantic names representing hoped-for states of existence, such as Clearview or Day Dawn. Returned from the wreck of war, my father chose the name Spring Forest for his farm: there was new life (in the form of me, for a start), and a forest of eucalypts through which clear water seeped from

several little springs, in a good season, to make patches of
emerald grass (a magical, startling colour in the blue-grey
bush). We used the name Spring Forest in our letter-writing,
but in speech reverted to Hickey's. In speech, the old names
stuck; they had the most authority. Their owners' bones were
in the soil, along with stone axes left like warnings, turned up
by usurping ploughs.

Once, then, Conlan, whoever he was, had owned the paddocks slanting to the road that ran past Cameron's Reserve,
and in one corner near the road was Conlan's Swamp. Winter
map-makers would have marked it, but in summer it shrank
to a gleam of light in long dry reeds, like a broken slab of col-
ourless glassy sky. A few eucalypts stood around, old and
spare, used to a hard life, tapping deep into the hidden spring
that fed the swamp. In summer you could miss it completely,
except that a tall white bird — an ibis, egret or spoonbill —
often stood there, perfectly at home among the reeds. You
would look again and see that a blue-grey heron kept it company. The swamp was a staging post for waterbirds in the
heat-blasted countryside. Solitary travellers dropped down
and rested there. They looked benignly towards the water,
and struck with absolute precision at some squirming kind of
life below its surface.

I never approached Conlan's Swamp on foot, but gazed at
it from hurrying vehicles, lifting my eyes from whatever book
I was reading (some old number with cracking glue and des-
iccated silverfish from the high school library), instinctively
recognising the way light changed and skittered along beside
us as the hills fell away. I loved that swamp and those
waterbirds. I knew of the distances they travelled with a com-
pass of living tissue, how they made their headquarters each
year at the fabled Macquarie Marshes, further inland, in con-
vocations of thousands. I knew that some of the egrets sailed
over the backs of enormous fierce beasts gathered at African
waterholes, and how the ibis walked sideways along Egyp-
tian walls. I revered the untouchability of birds, their inde-
pendence of the ground.

Ten times a week we rushed past Conlan's Swamp in the
school bus, our shuttling prison that each day sweated and

strained with its load of farmers' children all headed for another day of doom at the two secondary schools in the town, styled on billboards as "the Gem of the Golden West". We had outgrown the little one-room, one-teacher, two pepper tree schools, to which we had walked or ridden, wandering through puddles and picking tobacco weed. Taller, we were consigned to the town, some to the state school and some to the convent, where boys learned football from gentle nuns who hitched up their black skirts and demonstrated drop kicks to future heroes of the game.

Scuffles, loud pointed whisperings, frantic last-minute learning of lines and chewing of chunky toast (cold with congealing butter) were sometimes interrupted by the cry, "Blue heron!" and the bus's embattled crew would be quiet for a moment, engrossed in the business of twisting around and peering through dusty glass, for we thought that the heron with its blue-grey storm-cloud colours was a rain-bringer, a messenger promising more temperate times. Someone on the bus had a relative who said so, anyway: "Me uncle Ray reckons them blue herons're a signa rain, for sure, you bet."

Noise and smells increased towards the back of the bus, where hard-edged school ports were planted in the aisle to trip up underdogs, or were suddenly flung from knees to floor with a crash, or were sat on for a lurching game of knucklebones (bones gathered from paddocks, which had once belonged to sheep). Surreptitious punches were thrown, and Foxy Clive, who would never sit up near the front of the bus, was always in tears so that his freckles blazed as if freshly varnished. People unpeeled the greaseproof paper from their sandwiches, lifted a corner of the bread and made disparaging comments about their mothers. Boys conducted farting and belching competitions, and the most daring passengers imitated the bus driver's facial tic: his mouth constantly twitched itself sideways as if pursuing his left ear, while his small eyes swivelled from road to rearview mirror in helpless contemplation of the chaos that pursued him, and was his livelihood.

Boys left the bus with ripped shirts hanging out, their ties and ports flung after them; heads hung from the windows like gargoyles, yelling things; sometimes vomit streaked the bus's sides, and yellow dust turned it to clay. Even the quietest girls had fingers ingrained with ink, and sweat and dust in their hair. It was a long trip, and everyone reached home in disarray. In winter, it was nearly dark when we got home. Chained dogs leapt and yowled, bucking against their collars as we bent to release them. There were steel springs inside them after a day on the chain; inside us was weariness. Hens needed food and water; firewood had to be found. Only a narrow strip of day remained to us between school and tea-time, when we would be corralled indoors again.

Late in the afternoons in town, the nuns held court in music rooms where state school children sometimes came for lessons. Walking down the main street past the Greek milkbars – the Gardenia, the Golden Key and the Garden of Roses – we went from the solid block of the high school to the convent's peaks and curves in darker brick, ornate with temperamental old European authority. "Every Good Boy Deserves Fruit" was one of the first things we learnt here, and we also learnt to avoid the hawk gaze of Mother Aloysius, who was said to be almost one hundred years old: certain hoary citizens, now in charge of produce stores, had been dandled on her knee in near-primeval times. Woe to the child whose knobby knees, scarred from falls off bicycles, stuck gracelessly into the aisles between the rows of desks (the desks all scarred as well); and woe to the child who could not answer the rapped-out questions about the behaviour of crotchets and quavers, not to mention demi-semiquavers, which apparently helped to make up music.

This was called Music Theory, but the only theory we clung to was that the round-bodied, long-legged blobs we drew in their five-barred cage should soar off the page like waterbirds, taking us with them. We heard celestial music played on the ABC on our ramshackle home radios powered by car batteries, music getting a look-in somewhere around the River Heights and the Train Times ("and the Mudgee-Binnaway-Gwabegar Mail is also running on time"). We felt but could not latch on to the marvellous knowledgability of music, and knew that it might have led us out of the thickets of uncertainty where our souls (whose presence we sensed but had not yet managed to verify) were stuck fast.

But the notes stayed silent, obstinate. They were trapped with us and would not fly. Mother Allie, pure and wrinkled as a windfall apple, was their keeper, and they were the hidden fruit that we did not yet deserve. Most of us gave up Music after a couple of years. Our fathers had suffered for us, leaving animals unattended and tractors cooling in half-ploughed paddocks, to come all the way to town in ailing unregistered utility trucks, so that we could, for one hour after school each week, cobble and struggle with the inky blobs, and force violins to emit the screams of banshees. The school bus claimed us after that, every morning and every afternoon.

Mr Hickey, when he and the schoolboys built our house, had been content with two rooms and a verandah, but I was desperate for privacy, and made my study headquarters in a Triumph Renown, one of the many old cars that were sinking into the ground near the house. They were used as spare-parts quarries, dog kennels and storerooms. Sometimes dead sheep lay stretched across their bonnets; in some, hens laid their eggs. The Triumph had come to rest under a eucalypt; it was peaceful and roomy. Here, with a glass of water on the dashboard and books across my knees, I did my homework while the summer light lasted, unravelling lines of Latin to find Horace praising the spring on his parched Sabine farm: "O fons Bandusiae splendidior vitro". I could see that animated water, that fluid crystal jumping in the Roman light. Outside, the paddocks baked tinder-dry and bristled with armies of grass seeds.

(Families of mice lived in horsehair caves in the Triumph's upholstery, and scattered their droppings across the seats like relics of a wild party; eventually they combined with a coven of redback spiders to drive me out. It was hot in there, anyway, and the cracked vinyl stuck to the back of my knees.)

As summer's heat intensified, we became obsessed with water. We could not walk past a rainwater tank without knocking on it to hear the low response, and saw how the knuckles of a human hand resemble a tank's curved corrugated iron, but could not say if the water reservoir was inside or outside ourselves. When rain clouds refused to form, we felt the misery of Sturt who carted a wooden boat on his expedition to the fabled inland sea, and abandoned it in a dry creekbed. Clipping coupons out of magazines passed on through a chain of relatives, I sent for free travel brochures and gazed at the tiny photographs of lakes and islands, and villages growing in dazzling crystalline clumps around a bay.

In the main street of the town, the young Greeks stood in the doorways of the milkbars, looking out. John from Ithaca, Jimmy from Lesbos, Spiro from somewhere in the Cyclades — how fortunate they were; they were gods, or next to gods. Horace and his mates often talked about the places they came from. It was not cooking grease that anointed their dark glossy skin, as some people said, but the shine of legendary pure water. Behind them the cavernous dark cafes were cloudy with airborne oil molecules like sea-spray; the liquid crackle of deep-frying chips was waves breaking on rocks known to Ulysses. The young Greeks stared out across the street at Reid Smith's and Fossey's department stores, and watched the heat haze rising from the tar.

We knew, Horace and I and all other people living on farms, that water was life: it was also spiritual life, and islands, gardens, rivers and seas of stories. Drought meant death, or at least a shutting-down, a conserving of strength for the battle. From the chaos of the school bus I waited each day to see the rounded bodies of the long-legged waterbirds drifting like airships above the hidden face of Conlan's Swamp. They had what my life lacked: the ability to soar and survey and find sustaining water. At home in the opposite worlds of earth and sky, they were signs of hope — hope for all things, not just for rain.

And our bus kept on careering with its crooked-faced driver along its route, which was supposed to be the path of enlightenment, to the places of learning where discipline was often so strict that it paralysed thought. Music, and Mathematics too, had beaten its wings and died somewhere between the concrete stairwell and the shiny pale-green walls, with the framed and faded prints of Van Gogh's hot sunflowers and somebody else's blue horses, and the desk lids under which lurked screwed-up Kleenex tissues and swollen chewing gum. On the desk lids were carved the forlorn (though once defiant) initials of a past pupil (likely to be the cousin of a neighbour), now a grown man but still unmarried – well, he'd tell you there wasn't all that much to choose from – working on his father's land; he would sometimes be seen behind the wheel of a truck on a rare trip to town, his face weathering like a dry red rock.

Then one year, during the long summer holidays, the farmer who owned the land ploughed and filled in Conlan's Swamp, and it vanished completely, like a cloth flicked from a table, stripped and shaken. The waterbirds never came back. The trees were cut down too. Nothing was left except bare ground.

Armidale: No Palo Alto

Alex Buzo

When my family decided to move to Armidale it was a trauma and a calamity. "How will I be able to follow my radio serials?" I reasoned with my parents. Nevertheless, on a clear day in August 1951 we arrived in Armidale and had our first dinner sitting on packing cases in the living room. The radio was plugged in and I heard my serials, even though Sydney was 360 miles away. "Seahound ahoy!" cried the watch, and he could have been standing in the next room. I was ecstatic. Perhaps this town would not be the cultural desert I had imagined.

The next night the radio reception was terrible. My father rigged up a long aerial that went to the top of the gum tree in the backyard but it made no difference. Occasionally on a still night we could pick up the magic words "McDowells of King and George Street Sydney presents Superman", but you can't follow a serial that way; the narrative and the subtext become mysteries and all you get is cheap, momentary sensations. I had to abandon ship and come to terms with life in the country; we were going to be here for a while, and the static-prone radio was not going to help.

It rained the first day I went to Ben Venue Public School, as it has rained on the first day I have started every educational institution. When I started at the University of New South Wales in 1963 it rained for weeks, just in case I switched courses. At Ben Venue there were two classes per room, and the teacher would give a lesson on one side, set some work, and then move over to the other. If you started talking when the other side was "on", then you risked decapitation. Most of the teachers could keep talking as they hurled whatever was to hand at any "pest" on their off side. By far the best shot was a volatile, dedicated enforcer called

"Brick" Barnes (his nickname referred to his red hair) who quickly won complete silence.

As a new boy I had to adjust to the company of those who had never heard of Biggles. They listened to clear-as-a-bell Radio 2AD, where the popular drama was *Dossier on Demetrius*, a kind of cloak-and-dagger soapie. We all thought the title was *Dossier and Demetrius* and that it was about two spies, one of whom was always mysteriously absent. One boy at the school with a penchant for evil-looking pocket-knives was given the nickname Dossier. It stuck to him like fly-paper, so much so that teachers marking a roll would call out "Dossier Walsh?"

Ben Venue was on the northern fringe of Armidale, attracting children from small farms and the houses along the highway. The road outside our house was dirt, however, and the milk was delivered by horsedrawn cart. It was un-refrigerated, unpasteurised, and left in a billycan on top of the fencepost, where in winter it turned to yellow ice. Most of the houses in the town were weatherboard and had no hope of keeping out the cold. They looked as if they had all been built during a heatwave in 1947, when bricks and thought were severely rationed. If early houses in the rest of Australia were not built to cope with the heat, it was the reverse in the highlands of Armidale, where people would sit about in Canadian jackets in the living room and wear polo-necked jumpers to bed.

The drab Yankophilia of the early fifties could be seen in the framed colour pictures of Gene Autry on living room walls and the squawks of delight when the 1953 Ford Customline was unveiled and coveted by half the town. Sheet music from MGM foot-tappers abounded. I used to suffer from Armidalitis – about two-thirds of the way into the school term and live for the holidays, when my mother would take my brother and me back to Sydney.

Although my father held a Master's degree in Engineering from Harvard, he was thirty nine before he got his Big Toy: a dam to build. What had brought us to Armidale was the Oaky Hydro-Electric Scheme and it took until early in 1956 before the turbines went to work. Sometimes my father would accompany us to Sydney, driving the car through the exotica of Chilcott's Creek, Lambing Gully, Dunduckety Creek, Commissioner's Waters, Chilcott's Swamp, Goonoo Goonoo, Doughboy Hollow and Poison Swamp Creek. The life and variety of Sydney would be spread out before us eight hours later. Armidale was not a monochrome hole; but it could never quite compete with the Big Noise, with its milk bars and harbour.

Topographically, Armidale has apparent unity, with North Hill and South Hill facing each other over an evenly formed valley. The centrepiece, however, is an awful anti-climax which goes by the name of Dumaresq Creek (pronounced Dew Merrick, to rhyme with numeric). This winding, spiteful little tract of what purports to be water has long been a town joke. It was what originally attracted settlers to the area, but for years it has been a grudging conveyor of oil and effluent. In floodtime it swells across roads and parks and forms a wide brown band through the valley, stopping just short of Beardy Street, the main drag and centre of Armidale's cafè society.

Some people believe that the purity and calm of Angloid Australia was left undisturbed until it was shattered by the arrival of boatloads of uninvited wops in 1949. Unfortunately for the dreamers, pre-war Australia was probably never the paradise they imagined. Armidale certainly was not, and many long-established businesses in the main street were owned by people of Greek or Syrian descent. Indeed, so successful and influential was one of these business proprieters that Armidale became known in some circles as Joe Hanna's Burg. The atmosphere was definitely not "multicultural", despite these diverse backgrounds. Garlic was a prohibited import until about 1961, and at the Minerva Cafe Mr Rologas would serve you steak and eggs. Basic English was always spoken.

One of the shops in the main street, flanked by Jury's and Sourry's, was John Greet Mercer. I never heard the word mercer used in conversation. No one ever said, "John Greet's one of the best bloody mercers you'll ever see", nor did they ever sign off with "I'll just pop in here for a bit of mercer". Mercer was part of the secret-public language which was

seen and not heard. There were many other examples of this
suburban-genteel language that never caught on in Armidale
– pharmacy, spectacles, commence, attend, venue, millinery
– and you just knew that it would always be chemist's,
glasses, start, go to, place, hats for as long as rural Australia
existed. Afternoon, too, was not always afternoon, but this
arvo, while this evening was known locally as the seve. The
swimming pool, where I was taught to swim by Olympian
John Monckton, was the bars or pee soup.

The fashion for giving sporting arenas stolid names did not
end with Sydney Cricket Ground or Melbourne Cricket
Ground. In Dumaresq Street you could find Rugby League
Park, where Armidale did battle every second Sunday. On
cold days, that is, every Sunday, most of the spectators
stayed in their cars on the specially banked northern end.
There would be rows of Customlines and Zephyrs and
Holden utes full of silent faces staring out through the
windscreens like fish at an aquarium. Then when Armidale
scored, the honking of the horns would tell the world. You
could be chopping wood two miles away and be able to follow
the score. The muted reaction to an opposition try was even
more subdued if the team came from a long way away. The
nearby town of Guyra was noisily supported but Moree usually scored in near-silence. One woman sitting in front of a
muddy car once offered me a bribe to barrack for her team.
She was a fan of the Moree centre, Eric Bonser, and would
yell out "Bonser! Bonser!" with its tone of built-in approval
whenever the ball came near her idol.

From a vantage point behind the north fence you could
watch the game free. This area was known, inevitably, as
Scotchman's Hill, and the league planted pines to impede
these freeloaders. Unfortunately by the time they grew the
game was moribund in Armidale, killed by Rex Mossop and
his telecasts from Sydney, as well as a better road to the
coast, where Valla Beach became known as Little Armidale
because of its ghetto of weekenders. Walking across Rugby
League Park now, I can still hear the horns honking, and the
voices – "I'll give you threepence if you cheer for Moree" –
and the wonderful characters in those teams of the fitties: Big

Ron Potter, Brians Marquart and Gream, Trevor Hong, Richie Clutterbuck and "Sober" Beresford, all of whom wore the green jersey every second cold Sunday in what was the district's real amphitheatre.

Many of the smaller towns, such as Warialda and Walcha, used to take delight in tossing the Greens and were rather inclined to think of them as Big Sheilas. Although Armidale did have the biggest population in the area it was unfair to think of the team as being "advantaged" when it came to brawn. A lot of this population was academic or seasonal or both. In the thirties, when the University of New England was just a college, Armidale was much less of an Athens of the North. Everyone turned out for the Greens, and they were a major source of folklore. According to legend, when rugged kingpin Joe Hanna was knocked out in one pre-war game, his father Moses rushed on to the field. "Oh God," he wailed, "take my wife. Take my shop, even. But please spare my Joey." Joe recovered and went on to represent New England before his thoughts turned to owning it.

The captain of the 1954 Greens was Ron "Posso" Madden, who was an all-round athlete. He represented the district at cricket, and I once saw him batting at the showground. He was in the process of butchering a spin attack before an empty grandstand and, after hitting successive boundaries, was rewarded with a "Good on you, Posso" from a laconic spectator. "Why do they call him Posso?" I asked. "Because he's real wily," I was told. "He's as cunning as an old possum." We then had to take cover as another subtle gambit of Posso's cleared the fence. The Armidale XIII had a noisy and triumphant 1954, defeating West Tamworth in the grand final, and Ron Madden was a hero. Roy Brislan, the excitable bow-tied manager of 2AD, was in heaven. His biased calls of the big games were legendary ("Armadillo's on the attack" he would bray, as the battered Greens took a goal-line dropout) and this premiership triumph was his best Sunday. It was slowly, but all, downhill after 1954; Roy Brislan died of a heart attack before colour television dealt the final blow to the fading Greens.

By early 1956 I was rather hoping that with the Oaky

Scheme having opened in a torrent of glory we might pack up and go back to Sydney. My father, however, thought the country was the place for engineers and started a private practice, building bridges and roads around New England as well as in obscure beachheads like Oberon and Mullumbimby. I had to start secondary school and it not only rained on my first day there, it flooded. My mother rang the school and told me, "The bridge is under water. You'll have to spend the night at the Storys". I had to doss down on the verandah of classmate and future economist Ian Story's place as the rain kept on coming and Dumaresq Creek resembled the estuary of the Amazon.

By December it had dried out and I had to help my father survey a bridge site in Walcha. This clashed with the Olympic Games and I would drop the staff every so often and run back to the car and the radio through the heat and the flies to hear how John Monckton was doing in the pool in Melbourne. "John's won his heat!" I would yell out. But alas, Armidale's favourite son ended up with a silver medal and the gold went to the South Australian backstroker David Thiele.

Another famous export from the area whom I knew around this time was Peter Allen, then Peter Woolnough, who played the piano at high school dances. Although we went to different schools, he lived near me and I used to borrow books from his extensive library. He was mad about MGM musicals – which were hopelessly dated even in 1957 – and would tell you the plots endlessly. Although there was some question about whether he could sing or play in tune, there was no doubt about his almost religious sense of vocation. He was going to be an entertainer. By the time he was thirteen he had been studying the business for ten years. Like Ecuador's Sir Frederick Ashton and South Australia's high flier Sir Robert Helpmann, Allen came from an obscure part of the world, was not really very gifted, but succeeded through his will to win. The modern audience appreciates that when the desire to entertain eclipses the ability to entertain the result can still be legitimately entertaining. Peter Allen successfully imposed his 1949 MGM sensibility on the eighties because he really wanted to. He also cares about his audience and makes them feel part of the conspiracy to defeat God-given talent. The sheet music for his classics "I Still Call Australia Home" and "Tenterfield Saddler" is now prominently on sale in Armidale.

By 1958 I was a teenager and one of Armidale's huge school population. The city of churches and schools, hedges and colleges had its own Pop Tate's, and the young tribes used to gather at Comino's IXL Cafe. The news from the IXL was almost always bad. The girl around the corner you admired was seen in one of the booths there with the school captain, it was gleefully reported.

The major Catholic school was De La Salle College, known in the town as Dee-lah or College. In my first week at the Gothically Protestant TAS, I made the mistake of referring to "College" in front of a prefect. "We don't call it College here," he reproved me. "Dee-lah, then?" No, not even that. The correct expression was Tykeland. Of course, this was in the middle fifties, when sectarianism was very much the thing. We only had dances at equally Anglican NEGS, where the TAS Walk was employed, a kind of catatonic stroll, or Fourex Pavane — and you struggled desperately to find something to say to the girl of your fifth choice. Years after I left, a new generation of TAS boys challenged the old verities by breaking into St Ursula's Convent.

My wife, who was at Armidale High School during this period, nearly cried when she learned in 1987 that the IXL was to be demolished and an arcade would take its place. I was quite dry-eyed and explained to her that my father designed the arcade, using techniques from bridge-building. "I hope you were well paid, Dad" was all I had to say on the subject. I was rather suspicious of my wife's lament for long afternoons in the IXL booths spent sipping Mr Comino's excellent icecream sodas. My father's long career had several myth-demolishing overtones: he had designed the sewerage system for Dimboola in 1940.

The first beer I had was a Grafton Lager at the golf club There were no drugs when I was a teenager. If, however, you saw a female Teachers College student smoking, it was a pretty sure thing that she "went off". Once I saw a student teacher with good legs smoking and swearing at the golf club and I was absolutely certain she went off. Although occasionally you could see people climbing up the ivy to the balconies at the Teachers College hostel, Armidale's growing student population was very well behaved all through the Menzies years. For one thing, they knew all about the Town and Gown derby and did not want to get too far off-side with the people who sold them food and drink. The Town people were concerned, among other things, that the "university types" did not mow their lawns – and that affected property values. A big hurdle for the wearers of the Gown was the causeway in Dumaresq Street they had to cross to get out to the university. Whenever the creek was up, according to the Town, those "university types" got caught on the causeway and had to be towed. They couldn't judge the speed they needed to attack the rising water, or when it was prudent to go the long way round.

Other tensions in the town started to become more apparent around this time. East Armidale was known as Darktown because of its high proportion of Aborigines. Black pride was not quite as strong then. Now they have their own football team, Narwan, led by stalwarts Billy Ahoy and Bimbo Widders. No one calls them the Darktown Strutters any more. The East End also had the racecourse and the Wicklow Hotel, and the social cost of these two institutions could be seen in the poor areas of West Armidale, where dinner would often consist of "devon" and tomato sandwiches, all bought on credit. Some conflicts were more basic: locals cannot recall a day that has passed without two cars running into each other at one of Armidale's hundred blind intersections. The city is laid out on two remorseless grids running east-west and north-south, with the creek providing the only geometric relief. Frosted windscreens and poor street lighting ensure that people keep running into each other. Armidale is the opposite of Los Angeles, with no freeways or through roads. Even the highway runs right through the town. If you nominate any two families in Armidale, there is sure to have been a collision between them at some time.

However "ethnic" the town may have been, the brown

belt around Armidale, the putative "New England", was profoundly Angloid. It didn't look anything like England, of
course, with its brown fields and silver gums, but often you
would hear That Voice, a game stab at an Oxford accent, the
kind of air-giving warble that is common in Adelaide. More
frequent, though, is the sound of patrician Australia, a pleasant but insistent drawl that gets louder as its owner grows
older. The viyella set used to stay at Tattersall's Hotel when
they came to town, but Tatts is now an Aboriginal hang-out
where you never hear That Voice.

In between the town and the country lie that happy hybrid
lot, The Outskirters. These people can be found living on the
outskirts of many country towns, but in Armidale they have
had the place surrounded. To be an Outskirter you need a
couple of acres, a house with a prominent fireplace, two rows
of cabbages, and a car in the backyard with its boot open. I
have never really been sure why *every* small property just out
of town has a car parked in the yard with its boot open. Is it
some kind of freemasonry? Perhaps a closed boot would be a
sign of defiance. The Outskirters maintain a polite but firm silence on the question.

Have all these social differences remained intact? It is hard
to say. It was certainly a proud day for Armidale's I-ties when
Alderman Claude Cainero was sworn in as mayor, but he was
a bachelor with his eye on a National Party seat and he left the
district without issue. As for the Town and Gown imbroglio,
I caught up with that in April 1988. I was buying wine at a li-
quor store which had a large selection. In the fifties, buying
wine would have been a sure sign that you were a "university
type", but not any more; now everyone drinks wine. I handed
the bottle confidently to the proprietor at the counter.

"Are you up for the Graduation?" he asked, reeking of subtext.

I suddenly remembered I was wearing a check shirt. "Oh
no," I explained. "I'm here to visit my parents."

I moved back to Sydney in 1960, but since my parents
"retired" to Armidale in 1974, I have been back at least once
a year. The swimming baths turned green with plankton in
the seventies but they have now been replaced by a sparkling

blue aquatic arena with the (inevitably) boring name of Armidale Swimming Centre; De La Salle and St Ursula's merged into O'Connor High. A retail boom rendered the old weatherboards obsolete, but there are three houses that remain unchanged and aloof. The first is on North Hill and was built with post-war used-car money. It still glows with confidence and pride at having introduced the double garage to the Dumaresq valley. Behind it and up the hill a bit is a thin reddish, two-storey wooden-framer that looks like a Connecticut barn that has been concertinaed. An Aboriginal family called Widders lived there before the war in respected isolation. Later they were built out and moved, but their reedy maroon chapel remains. On top of South Hill the beauty of Soudan is also untouched. Soudan is over a hundred years old and broods behind a high hedge, its gun-metal brick unfaded. Is it haunted? I always thought so. Armidale does have its legends.

Now a city of 24,000, the old place is gradually taking on its own character – almost alpine in its cold, semi-learned, clean way, full of tall trees that riot in spring and autumn, brick and plaster, sealed roads and (long silence) pasteurised milk, a university town of well-run small business which caters for graziers and panel-beaters and the old at heart. Armidale is not yet New Haven, South Bend, Palo Alto or either Cambridge; but it has long since proved it is not Coober Pedy.

You Will Know His Creatures

Susan Johnson

You will know His creatures from the valley below, said the preacher, or I think he did. The sweat is gathering behind my knees certainly, trickling now and then down the backs of my calves. This preacher has buck teeth and the church is hot: my father has said when I am sixteen I can decide for myself whether I will come to Church, or not. Or not.

Outside, the grass is breaking.

You will go to school, certainly. The bus will drive past the gate of your farm Monday to Friday and you will climb on. The bus looks like a tourist coach, with little blue curtains bunched at each window. I have never had a bus halt at my door before with the express intention of picking me up, but then again until this moment I have never lived on a farm. A farm! There are creatures in the valley but everywhere silence, or stealth. A farm! The fruit grows on the tree and your father says, In summer you can help the boys pack fruit. The boys are my three brothers and, yes, pocket money is what we want.

I feel embarrassed every morning when I climb on the bus. You are from another world and your shoes are too new.

You will say, I am from Sydney and it will sound like, Take Me To Your Leader. You will live inside an invisible barrier: there will be you, and outside this barrier, the world. You will covet the lips of the handsome school captain and will live to witness the day when he winks at you during morning assembly. You will get slapped on the wrists by the headmaster who will shout, You may very well be from the city, young lady, but in this school when you speak to a teacher you put your hands behind your back. And call me Sir!

Later I think I heard that this man killed himself. You might think: Did he use a gun? Did he strike out his eye at one go?

You will watch a creature of the valley on its mission to kill your father. You mother will say, Get your father a towel, because she can hear him calling from the bathroom and assumes it is what he wants. You will reply, Oh, Mum, but when she says it a third time you will take a towel from the closet and go out the back door to the bathroom outside. An outside bathroom! You will hear your father calling, Elaine! You will hear your mother replying, It's coming! But when you get to the bathroom you will see a snake making its way to the space at the top of the door and you will scream, Mum! And Mum and your three brothers will come at once and your oldest brother will rush for a spade. When the snake is lying with its head smeared on the concrete your father will come out of the bathroom with a towel wrapped around his waist and say, I didn't need a towel.

You will cry in your bed for your lost life. You will cry in the arms of your father because, for girls, the schools in this state only offer Academic or Commercial and you have never done French, or Typing. You will cry because you have to wear on your head a stupid hat and listen to "God Save the Queen" every morning at school assembly. You have heard that the creatures of the valley kill within three minutes and that it is a long way to Sydney.

Your mother and father will look over your head at each other.

You are a girl with too much imagination, certainly.

Your youngest brother will bring home baby snakes, and chickens, though not at the same time. His feet will become weathered and his speech slow: he will grow up to hate cities. Perhaps he is nine, or ten, when he comes to the country. A farm! Can I drive the tractor, he will ask. Can I sleep in my tent outside at night, alone? He will learn to read the sky and interpret the wind. His friends for ever after will always be drawn from the few miles within this same radius.

You will find yourself too old or too young for the place, a teenaged girl practising exile. How does it feel to be an emigrant? How does it feel to be in the wrong place? You will begin your search for the right place, a long search, although you don't yet know it.

You will come to have a reputation as stuck-up. Girls will jeer, but you will pretend not to hear. You know it has something to do with the self-conscious gait of your body and the way dreams leave their debris in your eyes. By way of compensation you will begin to smile a lot, and and discover how to wage war without blood.

You will learn to make the school captain weep. He will wear white shorts and you will roll with him in the grass: he will ask, Will you marry me? but you won't answer because you are only fifteen. In your mind's eye you can see London and Paris and Rome: you are certainly imagining the lot.

You will learn to drive a Jeep, to climb avocado trees, to scare possums. You will learn to play golf using cane toads as the ball. You will discover that the beautiful view from the farmhouse windows becomes unreal very quickly and you can no longer appreciate its beauty. Years later, when you hear a man speak of his wife's beauty as being invisible to him, you will know what he means. When guests arrive at your farm you know they will inevitably cry, oh! the view! but you dare not tell them that your eyes no longer see.

Outside, you know that the view is inhabited by creatures. Outside, the valley is too still for comfort and the bush, to you, will always be too lonely.

At the end of the first school year you will win the Citizenship Education prize. You will wear a white dress and climb the steps of the stage to collect the prize from the smiling headmaster. You know the difference between preferential

voting and first past the post. Does this mean you are now educated to be an active citizen? Will you correctly negotiate the
lie of the land and enter the world knowing how to stay out of
jail?

And when you finally turn sixteen you will tell your father
you no longer wish to go to Church.

I no longer wish to go to Church, you will say. You will say
it, just like that.

It will not be long after this that you move to the city to
continue your search for the right place. It is only natural you
do not look back.

Mothers and Old Lovers

Gillian Mears

Our dog died on Christmas Day and Dad made us dig the hole.
You would've needed a crowbar to get it deep enough, the
ground was that hard and we had to be ready by eleven for
Erica's Christmas lunch. So Dingus was popped into the back
corner of the garden and at the time it hadn't seemed to matter that his legs stuck out. He was a tall dog. It was too hot to
cry.

Today Dad says I ought to mow the lawn as he's invited
Erica, on the spur of the moment, to a Boxing Day barbecue.
For Christmas he'd given us each a green garden rake and
not much else. To pay him back Kate withheld the box of
chocolates she'd picked out weeks ago for him. Matt disguised his disappointment by racing downstairs with a giant
tin of dog food for Dingus – a special Christmas treat. He
found Dingus stiff and sprawled out underneath the house.
We nearly cried then. I could feel the temptation for tears
creeping slyly and steadily up all our throats: as overwhelming as the stink of dog food that Matt kept clutched to his
chest. Kate stayed quiet, concentrating on eating as many
melted liqueur creams as possible; her eyes went shiny with
waiting tears.

Dingus was Mum's dog but she'd left him behind with us
when she went; one Saturday morning in the middle of hanging out the washing when we were all down at the river. She
left the goodbye note pegged to the line. It was a drip-dry
load. Her thumbprint was watery and smudged over the bit
about Mathew taking good care of Dingus. Dad said she'd be
back, but after a week the clothes left in the trolley under the
clothes hoist went grey with mildew.

It's the worst job, mowing our lawn in summer. Our house
is on a huge corner block, plus there's the levee at the back to

be tackled last, just when you're most weary. I decided to begin back to front and do the levee bank first. Dad insists Kate and Matthew stand by with their new rakes. And he's so mean, saying a snake probably bit Dingus because of the long grass he'd asked me to mow two weeks before Christmas.

At the bottom of the long slope, the river glimmers deep and blue. The Pearce kids from up the road are at the jetty already. There is a big orange inflatable raft that must be one of their presents and a miniature electronic power boat that little Blur Pearce keeps sending in crazy loops around the jetty.

Dad said we'd appreciate a swim much more after the lawn was cut. And he suggested taking Erica for a sail after lunch, as if this were some sort of spectacular reward. He was in a terrible mood, having gotten half-charged at Erica's Christmas do. I'd say her punch was responsible; some horrible brew she insisted I could drink. "You're old enough to have a second glass." The punch was fermented and she hadn't bothered cutting the bruises from the strawberry and pineapple pieces floating on top. "Just help yourself Human, Hugh Mann." She has always made this ridiculous play on my name. "Go on Hughie. Your father isn't even looking our way."

She adds "ie" to all our names. Dad is Johnnie. Mum would never have let Dad get the mower out the day after Christmas. She hated it enough on ordinary weekends and always our lawn was the long shaggy green one next to the manicured efforts from either side. Now Dad wants to be indistinguishable from all the rest. There's even a dusty bed of marigolds along the side fence. Erica put them in at the beginning of summer. She tries too hard, arriving at unexpected hours with new ideas for the house and garden. Dad won't say anything but we suspect she'll be moving in soon. It's an awful future we've silently agreed not to discuss. But it hangs between us in the hot summer air and threatens to drop any day now. She only rents the house in Georges Drive, an asbestos shack, we tell Mum descriptively in our letters, surrounded by more nasty marigolds. Erica has told Dad the lease is about to expire. She's just waiting for Dad's enthusiastic suggestion.

Nothing is quite as bad as mowing over the top of fresh or not so fresh dog shit, but it's worse doing it, knowing that Dingus is dead. I know Matty felt the same yesterday having to mop up the circle of dog sick, remnants of Dingus's Last Supper — with the watery shape still very clear on the concrete. There'll probably be no replacement pup because Erica never seemed much good if Dingus came flying round a corner, tail thwapping to greet her. Instead, her two fat old cats will move in. They're grey Persians called Sheikh and Cleo, who will do their business in what's left of Mum's herb garden. Kate tried to kill them off yesterday, feeding them turkey fat and plum pudding but this tactic didn't appear to have worked by the time we left.

I mow in horizontal lines. Dad's Victa is old and battered. It's all clogged up with rotten grass clippings, and odd bits of wire and string tie it together. The catcher gave up operating a long time ago so Katie and Matt have to traipse behind me with their stupid new rakes. Dad never knew what to get us for Christmas. He always left the choosing to Mum really, but wrote a separate Christmas card — usually on some inappropriate leftover postcard that he'd scribble on in the hour before we were allowed to start unwrapping. We know automatically who must've suggested this year's gift idea.

"Something practical, Johnnie," I can hear Erica pointing out the specials in the hardware shop. "Keep them out of mischief. All children like to be helpful." She wouldn't know the first thing about us. The brightly wrapped presents she handed out after lunch yesterday were such a cheat. They looked quite good from the outside but she must've spent all her money on the wrapping paper. Everything was from the new pink stationery shop that smells of soap. For ten-year-olds, not teenagers. There were twelve texta colours for Matt; a geometry set for me with flowers on the tin and an airmail pad for Kate. On Erica's white tinsel tree hung three more small packages that she urged us to take. These turned out to contain pencil sharpeners and strawberry-flavoured erasers. Her presents made us think of school and how Christmas holidays never seemed very long any more. For Dad there was a long, elaborately wrapped mystery pack: just a lawn edger, a green lawn edger. Unbelievably, Dad gave her pearls.

In the paper last week it said the salt levels in the river have increased steadily to reach 900 parts per million and are as high as 1,200 ppm in some stretches of the river. As I mow, I search the water for fins. With salt levels so concentrated, there have already been a number of shark sightings. A kid from school caught a metre-long grey nurse using half a catfish for bait and his father's deep-sea fishing rod. We've been hopeful some nights from the jetty at dusk, thinking there's a swirl and a fin further off in the troughs of darkening water. But so far this holiday we've only caught catties and eels, as the giant river mozzies, who don't mind the taste of insect repellent, zoom in on our ankles. When Kate went canoeing with Blur, they passed right by six or seven small grey fins travelling upriver. Kate said they were so close she could've poked them with her paddle. It's the salty water bringing them from the sea to breed. You can taste the salt in the river shrimp we get with the Pearces' green net. We dare little Blur to eat them raw and he does, even chewing them instead of swallowing them down whole. He reckons they taste like new prawn-flavoured chips.

Every summer for as long as I can remember, the local paper runs a story about the increasing danger of swimming in the river. The trouble is no one's ever been eaten in the Fineflour. The full-page feature last year concentrated on the risks people swimming near the power station were taking – the argument being that the sharks concentrate there because of the warm waste water generated. But no one has even looked like being bitten. Such stories pale in comparison to the one paragraph that would appear a few weeks later about the Byron Bay surfer whose board was chomped in half by a huge great white: with nothing left of the holiday-maker from Sydney; not even a flipper.

*   *

Kate and Matt aren't looking at the river. They're making increasingly feeble efforts to pull grass clippings into order. Behind us are quite a number of pointy little grass piles but less than half the levee is done. Kate isn't high enough to work her rake properly and she lets it bump-bump behind her, her hat tipped up over fat pigtails. I cut the engine, let it cough dead. Dad will only think I am refilling with fuel.

"Blur must've got that boat for Christmas," says Kate.

"Let's piss off," Matt suggests. They drop their rakes and we fly down the hill. Matt is fastest. At the school carnival he was champion sprinter, doing less than eleven seconds for the one hundred metres. He doesn't look right without Dingus yapping along at his ankles. At the bottom, little Blur Pearce turns round to laugh at Mathew, "Still got your dick-stickers then!"

Mathew looks down at his old Speedos. They are way too small but he's wearing them because they were his favourite Christmas present from Mum last year. We're going to stay with her at Byron Bay in one week's time. *For a real Christmas*, she laughed, in the old way, down the wheezy public phone she always rings us on because every so often it dishes out free STD calls. She said she couldn't wait to see us, in a way that made you believe her. We'll eat at Mexican Mick's and have milkshakes for breakfast.

It's embarrassing being asked by the Pearces about presents. We're too ashamed to tell, so Kate diverts their attention by saying how good the raft is. She looks like Mum when she's being crafty: all innocence but her brain working double-time. Knowing the Pearces always spend Christmas holidays at home, she starts rattling on about the time we're going to have in Byron. She waggles her head cutely and then goes tearing along the jetty to dive-bomb over the new raft. Matt spits out a well-chewed piece of gum, puts it in Blur's hair and follows Kate.

From the lukewarm river, the metal of the lawn-mower glinting less than halfway down the levee makes us guilty. Matt and Kate's rakes lie like stiff casualties in an abandoned battle.

Dad probably hasn't realised we've gone yet. I can picture him hunched over the kitchen bench making a mess of the kebabs; using onion-flavoured fingers to chop the pawpaw for the fruit salad. Later today, Erica will smile encouragement at him as she pretends to enjoy the food and calls him Johnnie. When only last Christmas he was Jo, very short for Jonathon and there was no fussy Boxing Day barbecue; only a picnic of leftovers under the poplar on the ragged lawn that in those days Dad couldn't care two hoots about.

Erica isn't the first lover but she's definitely the worst. All of them have seemed older than Mum, with no kids of their own. But Dad has always been attracted by this older style of desperation. Even before Mum left, we noticed. At big dinner parties we'd snake out in our pyjamas to get secret fistfuls of leftover cashews. Peering through the window into the dining room, we'd see how the women leant against him, lurched fat thighs under the table, while from the kitchen Mum giggled to see our three heads popping up, too absorbed in us or whatever was cooking, so never seeing Dad. The morning after, we'd creep past their bedroom in search of abandoned after-dinner mints. There was the sad smell of empty chocolate boxes and they slept far apart, as if dropped, on opposite sides of the bed.

A game of water tag is about to begin when Elizabeth Pearce sights the stormy figure striding over the levee. From where we hide behind the orange raft, we can see the hangover from Erica's punch thumping round his head. Blur informs us that our dad looks wild as a bull ant the way he's waving his arms about.

"Wave back," whispers Kate, who floats, plump belly up.

"Jeese. I don't think I should've done that," Blur giggles.

"He's picking up the rakes. Oh. You're okay. He's starting the lawn-mower."

"The old poop," says Matt.

We hear the roar of the engine and try not to look at our angry father belting back and forth, back and forth. Kate pretends oblivion, clambering out of the water to sunbake on the wet wood boards, with her bottom pointing his way; her face watching the waves from a pair of water-skiers heave and flop against the jetty.

The only way to ignore him completely though, is to sink deep below the soft surface, into the cold, living levels. The water fills your ears and you hope and fear to see a shark when you open your eyes deep down. As usual, there's only green light and bubbles and the yellow look of your own feet, dislocated and lost in the river. There's something comforting though, feeling the water stream and flow past, with the buzz of a motor boat receding and receding in the back of your head. I make myself concentrate so that I can pee through my swimmers. It's like this thin warm current passing between your legs. After coming up for air, the sky looks bleary blue. Dad is disappearing with the mower to do the front lawn, the dumb sucker.

"He's still woopy," said Kate. She looks funny with her hair flattened by the water. Her face is round and egg-like. Mum said we were all easy to push from her body. Just like popping three eggs out, she said, and seeing Kate's head I can see what she meant.

"What's the time, Blur?" asks Kate.

"Eleven thirty and forty-four seconds past," he flourishes a new waterproof watch on his wrist.

"Bugger it. Better go back up, I suppose," Kate says glumly. "He'll probably make us do all the raking still."

Matt isn't listening. He's churning backward somersaults, trying to break his own record of twenty in a row. Every two turns, his mouth flies open, gulping like a goldfish. Matt dislikes Erica the most — ever since Dad let her go into the bathroom to use the mirror when Matt was having a bath. He hates her because she laughed at him. It was a few weeks after his appendix operation and oddly enough his pubic hair, which had only recently started to grow, began to come back bright red instead of blond.

The slide night was another reason for hatred. Erica insisted she wanted to see what we all looked like as babies. She left Dad no choice, turning up one evening with her projector and a bottle of port. We were getting ready to watch a program on sharks with incredible live footage of someone being eaten. Unbelievably, Dad made us switch the television off and talk to her as he rummaged about for some slide cartridges already loaded. His mistake. There were heaps of Mum with us in nappies or watching us toddle about with old Harry the cat dangling oversized from our arms. And then on the second cartridge, there were a whole lot of just Mum, naked except for a lemon scarf in her hair and much more beautiful than Erica.

Our mother has nut-brown nipples and is brown all over. On the white beaches she looks like a girl. Last time we visited, we all went surfing in the nude. She laughed like crazy at Matt's bright growing hair. We all laughed – so much that the muscles in our stomachs ached and ached. She asked a bit about Erica. We called Erica the old Sniffler or the Wrinkled Prune and felt guilty and good, treacherous and loyal, lying naked all together on the white, hot sand.

We can tell Mum is more at ease now that Erica has replaced Liz. Liz we didn't mind half so much. She was into acupuncture and naturopathy and made terrific felafel rolls complete with homemade hommos. The iced water in her fridge floated with aloe vera that looked like chunks of silver-glinting fish. Even Mum would enjoy the funny stories Liz used to tell. Like the one about old Percy Doyle who wanted acupuncture to get his penis working again after his last stroke. Liz was messy with an overrun garden and long, dangling earrings. Erica's so dull in comparison. Mum is secretly pleased, we can tell, when we try to outdo each other relating various boring things that Erica does – such as always using a silver bookmark to place in a book if she's interrupted and then placing the book back into its slot in her neat bookshelf.

At the slide night, Dad tried flicking through the ones of Mum quickly. This was his second mistake, because it made the projector jam. We could feel his desperation in the dark and the falseness of Erica's composure. Mum stayed standing on the far wall in a pair of light blue undies and nothing else. She looked better than any model and billowed a little towards us, as a breeze found the sheet Dad used as a screen substitute. Even with a lamp on, she stayed ghostly but visible, half-smiling at us until sniffling Erica turned on the main light and disappeared our mother from the room. The slide night resumed. Erica insisted it should and drank too much port as we kept appearing before her in different guises. Dad tried to flash quickly through the past: Mum with her face next to Dingus's, trying to imitate his dopey little puppy expressions; Matt and me in an inflatable backyard pool; Dingus as a pup at the beach; Kate drinking lime cordial in daggy green swimmers. From where I was sitting, I could look down Erica's dress to see a pair of old-looking breasts and the way her skin puckered and folded towards her neck. She smelt like a dying marigold — old and just a little bit sour.

It is noon exactly when we leave the Pearces' great Christmas presents and head up from the river. Kate's and Matt's noses are red. Their hair starts to dry quickly. Kate's is wild and crinkled after she lets her plaits out.

"Hey!" Blur says as we move off. "What've you done with Dingus? What did you give old Dingus dog for Christmas?"

"A snakebite," Matt ducks his head. "We reckon a snake got him. He was dead under the house yesterday."

"Oh. Gee, Dingus dead. Gee I'm sorry," Blur picks at the scabby bandaid hanging from his heel. "Are you going to have a funeral?"

"Nah, we had to bury him yesterday," Matt says. "Dad made us." He looks at the sky to stop the tears falling in front of little Blur Pearce.

Remembering Dingus makes us walk dully up the hill. Mum will have to be told her dog is dead, just when she'd found a place to rent that didn't mind animals. We were going to smuggle him on the bus with us to Byron Bay. Kate had bought an expensive blue collar with studs to make him look his best. As we trudge through the crazy furrows of Dad's mowing, the terrible thought stays unspoken; that Mum will think we've let her down. That Dingus died through some carelessness or neglect on our part.

"We should've brought up a few buckets of sand from the river to fix up Dingus's grave," Matt scuffs his feet in the grass clippings.

"Get it after lunch. Might as well," Kate says. "They always want us to piss off anyway." The angry crunch of the mower is louder as we approach the crest of the levee. It sounds as if Dad is attacking the straggling paspalum that grows under the tulip tree. The blades catch on the exposed roots, reaching and tearing into wet, green wood. The noise is worse than churning through the gravelly bits by the road — loose stones spitting out in every direction, into the skin of your ankles.

But Dad isn't doing under the tulip after all. He's going like a madman at the area near the pink hibiscus, which is where we chose to put Dingus. The mower screams and moans, attacking bone, nails and the soft paws Dingus would hold out to shake hands with. Dad is in a fury. The sweat pours off his face. His hair flaps with the momentum of the mower. He yells. He yells he's had enough. He yells he's fucking sick of it. He screams with the mower. The pink hibiscus that Mum loved so much because it gave her a tropical, holiday feeling and that flowered all through winter even, shakes and sheds flowers. I notice for the first time our father has a bald patch as the sun makes it glint and sweat. Dirt, grass and bits of white and pink gristle, mat in his hairy legs.

We wonder what Erica thinks, standing on our verandah behind our limp beach towels flung over the railing. As the mower starts to wheeze and whine and give up, we hear him more clearly.

"Fucking kids," he keeps propelling the failing mower back and forth on the splintery white bones that refuse to be cut down. "Bloody fuckwits."

Standing in a line of three on the levee, we gaze across our father to the bright floral figure still holding her handbag. Does she know it is Dingus? Does our father know she's there? We will her to turn and go. But she does the unexpected. She starts to laugh. That shrill staccato chuckle as Dad falls silent and the mower dies quickly.

A Little Candle Burning in the Night

Phyllis Gant

— Berta!

Aunt Em's weary voice.

— Here's Eustace now. Come and see if you can ride him.

A raw-boned horse with drooping head stands near the house.

— He's very quiet, says Aunt Em. Come here — I'll help you up. You won't need a saddle and bridle, you can tug at his mane. There you are now, off you go.

Eustace doesn't move a muscle.

— Go on, now. Gee-up! cries Aunt Em, giving the horse a slap on the rump.

He plods away towards the orchard. Roberta winds both hands in his mane and presses her legs against his skinny sides.

She slithers forward as Eustace stops and puts his head down. And she worms her way back along his bony spine. He walks under a tree, and she has to duck to avoid being dragged off. With the same resolute plodding, he takes her under another low-growing tree. Roberta lies flat along his back and, terrified, tugs at his mane.

Now he makes no pretence of walking about, but turns in his own length to push under and through the branches again. Roberta's face, arms and legs are bumped and scratched, and her dress is torn.

Again he turns about, pausing to look over his shoulder at the limpet on his back.

— You bad horse! cries Roberta. I *thought* you were doing it on purpose!

She tugs hard at his mane, not caring if it *does* hurt.

— Get out of that!

She jabs her heels into his sides.

– Gee-up, you!

Eustace turns away from the trees. Roberta tugs the left side of his mane, and he turns to the left: she pulls on the right-hand side, harder, longer: he turns right, turns right round as she keeps a steady pull until he is facing back towards the house. She sits straight and unafraid.

– Gee, I can ride a horse.

– Whee! and she stops him by the back porch.

– Aunt Em! Come and see! I can ride!

Aunt Em comes to the doorway.

– Oh, yes. Anyone can ride Eustace, she says. Eustace has taught lots of children to ride.

– Yes, well, he tried to drag me off his back, too. Look! and she shows her scratches. But I still rode him.

– Oh, you naughty old boy! says Aunt Em.

She pats Eustace's nose.

– But he doesn't mean any harm, my dear old boy doesn't. And he just loves children.

Roberta surveys the distance to the ground.

– Will you help me get off, please. Aunt Em?

– Ah, you have to learn how to get off a horse, too, Berta. Just hang on and bring one leg over and slide down his side near his foreleg. This way.

Roberta slides, landing on her behind on the ground. It doesn't matter that Aunt Em sees her. But that darned old horse –

He looks around, his head bent and his lip curled back, showing his yellow teeth.

Dear Mum and Dad. How are you getting on? I got here all right and Uncle Arthur came to meet me. Aunt Em has got very long hair it's that long she can sit on it. It was nice on the train a nice lady got out at a station and got us some chocolate. I gave her my sixpence for it and she gave it back to me because she said it was gotten free so that must be a nice place to live mustn't it. They don't have tea here till nearly the middle of the night. I can ride a horse now. I remain your ever-loving daughter Roberta. P.S. Aunt Em said to tell you I've said my prayers and she will see I don't forget I won't anyhow. P.P.S. Aunt Em said I can stay home for a week before I start school at this place she says she hopes you don't mind. I do too.

— You and Cliffie can play outside while Mrs Simpson and me have a nice talk. Cliffie could have a ride on Eustace if he likes. Berta, you catch Eustace and bring him up for Cliffie to ride. Excuse me, Mrs Simpson, won't you? I just haven't had time to do my hair yet — oh, and Berta, turn those apricots over on the racks for me, will you?

— They're covered with ants, Aunty!

— Brush them off, then.

— Two or three more hot days like this, says Emma to Mrs Simpson, and the fruit will be properly dried and we can get it away into the tins.

Eustace wants only to be left in peace. Roberta hauls him up from the orchard.

— There, she says, hot and bothered. See if *you* can make him move.

She turns to the apricots on the wooden racks. The fruit is wrinkled but still sticky. Roberta flicks the ants off each half and turns it over.

— This horse is no good. He's slow as a snail, says Cliffie.

— He's a lovely horse, says Roberta loyally. You don't know how to ride him, that's all.

— Listen to you talking about riding! says Cliffie. Townie! He slides expertly to the ground.

— Gee, that was smart, says Roberta. I just have to fall off.

— Did you see how I did it? says Cliffie. You sort of lean over and hang on till you touch the ground. Hey, I'll help you turn the apricots.

Then they wander to the tankstand, bored, climb up and rap at the tank to see how many rings of water are left.

— I wish I was a boy, says Roberta. It's better to be a boy.

— Oh, I dunno, says Cliffie. Yes, I s'pose it is.

— How old are you? says Roberta. I'm nearly nine.

— I'm nearly nine, too, says Cliffie.

Roberta loooks at her feet half-covered by the dusty soil,

pale and powder-fine, at the base of the tankstand. She wiggles her big toes.

— I've never seen a boy's.

Cliffie makes no answer, just watches her toes covering and uncovering themselves in the dust.

— D'you think you could let me see it?

Silence.

— I've never seen what one looks like.

Still no answer.

— Like, I don't want to be rude or anything. I just want to see what it looks like.

— No.

— Oh, go on. Please.

— No.

— Just a peep for a little minute, Cliffie.

— No.

— Don't be mean. I won't tell.

— No.

Recklessly, then.

— I'll show you mine.

Heart pounding.

— All right, Cliffie says.

— You go into the lav, says Roberta, then I'll come in.

Cliffie moves, dawdling, towards the lavatory, around the corner from the tankstand.

— Oh, hurry up! Roberta whispers after him, alarmed and wanting to get it over and done with quickly.

— You show me yours first, says Cliffie.

— No, you show me *yours* first, says Roberta.

Cliffie leans against the wall, arms folded.

— Oh, all right, then, Roberta mutters.

She lifts her dress and pulls down her pants.

Cliffie, his hands on his knees, bends and peers.

— Hurry up! cries Roberta. Haven't you looked enough yet?

— Yes. All right, says Cliffie.

Roberta hastily fixes her clothes.

— Now you show me yours.

— No, says Cliffie.

And bolts.
— You're rude, he calls.

— Of course she can't ride Lady. Lady's too frisky, says Em.
— She's got to learn to handle a horse some time, says Arthur.
— She's only a little girl, Arthur. Fancy you wanting to put her on Lady that takes me all my time to handle!
— Well, she won't be able to have Barney. I need him about the place. And Eustace'd drop in his tracks if she rode *him*. So she'll have to walk.
— Oh, Arthur, she can't walk all that way! It's too far for a child to walk all that way by herself!
— Well, damn it, woman, it'll have to be one or the other!
— Besides, says Em, how about if I want Lady? If Lady was quiet it'd be a different matter. But she'd throw the child the moment she felt a stranger on her back.
So Roberta must walk to school. Distressed. Emma combs her hair back with her fingers.
— I don't know. I really don't know. Perhaps we can get a pony for you later.
She takes Roberta along the track that leads to the school, out from the home paddock and to the boundary fence.
— I don't see how you'll manage this by yourself, Berta, she frets as she re-fastens the Gippsland gate. It's so hard to get the wire over the post . . . I think you'd better climb through with a bit of sacking on the barb wire.
Part of the way along the bush track, she draws a map on the ground with a stick, showing Roberta where the tracks fork, with one to the cemetery leading off on the left, and the sand track, which Roberta must follow, straight ahead.
Aunt Em puts her arms around Roberta and holds her tight. Roberta is rigid with distaste. Aunt Em, her voice quivering, mutters,
— God bless my little girl and keep her safe.

— Have you ever seen one of these? This is a jew lizard.
— And this is a blue-tongue. When they bit you you don't

die, it just leaves a sore that never gets better and it breaks out worse every year on the day you got bit.

Boys' laughter, sly, soft.

– God's truth.

– True as I'm here.

Grave.

Roberta intercepts a wink directed beyond her. She turns quickly to discover a boy with a writhing lizard in one hand, the other extended to take hold of the neck of her dress.

– Hey, what are you boys up to?

– Nothing, Mr Jeremiah. Nothing, sir. We're just showing the new girl some of the lizards we've got here.

– Well clear off. Boys will be boys, you know, he says to Roberta. Don't let them frighten you. They wouldn't really have put it down your back.

But would they, would they, would they have? The torment throbs in her brain.

Inside, Mr Jeremiah sets the work.

– Third grade work on the right of the left blackboard: sixth grade on the left. Fourth and fifth on the right blackboard. Melva, you go and hear the little ones their tables.

Mr Jeremiah settles at his desk with a book, turning the paper cover to the inside. But not before Roberta has seen the title, *True Detective Stories*.

True stories. I wish I could read that. It must be great to be grown up and read whatever you like.

Now and then Mr Jeremiah looks at his watch. Then he stands, stretches and yawns.

– Playtime, he says. Behave yourselves while I go and get my cup of tea.

He gets through a fence and walks quickly across the paddock towards a pine tree.

– His cup of tea, ha-ha-ha. We know all about his cup of tea.

– Come on, let's go and see if we can see him.

– Ah, you never see anything. It ain't worth wastin' the time.

– My old woman says he's carrying on with her that brings the tea.

– Yeah, an' one day when we watched 'em, remember? I told you! I seen him take out his horn.

– My old man reckons he's too old to do it even if he wanted to.

– Ah, come on, let's have a look.

Except for two or three older girls, the children crowd around the post at the corner of the fence. Melva calls the little ones to her and takes them into the playground.

– You come, too, Berta.

But Roberta, immobilised, stays on the fringe of the excited group by the fence.

– He's drunk his tea.

– Where! Where!

– We can't see him!

– Let *me* get up there.

The big boys on the post fights them off with one bare foot.

– Let him tell! Go on, what's he doing now?

– She's put the billy in the bushes. They're sitting on the ground.

– Where? Where?

– Hey, you'll push me off in a minute! He's standing up – look out! Let me get down, quick! He'll see me!

– What happened?

– What's wrong with him?

– Dunno. He's on his way back, anyhow. Come on, move! Get into the playground!

– Sir, can we go down the bush and play while you're away?

– We'll be careful of snakes, sir!

– Sir, me mother said when you go to the post office will you bring our mail, too.

– An' ours, too, sir!

Squealing, shouting, leaping like fiends. Wild they run.

The hot air is heavy with the scent of the tea-tree; the bush is still. Only the she-oaks rustle and whisper; they need no breeze to stir them. Scrub shudders as running boys disturb it or, with a shattering of the heat-hanging air, break it.

The girls, where are the girls? But some of them came running.

Roberta walks alone, outside the mystery. She must find them, see what they're doing.

Following the narrow bush tracks, watching for snakes (which the others, she reflects, seem to have forgotten about), she comes across some of the younger boys laughing and swearing, running about and grabbing at each other between the legs. Where are the big boys now?

The reality of the mother, unreal and far, far away. Strange, strange strangeness. And fear. And fear.

Sky, sun, hot smell of scrub. You can smell the wild honey.

Silence of the bush. Not even bees.

Lizards and snakes asleep.

You can't see them. But they're there.

She turns and runs, runs under the eye of the sun, runs until she is across the school track. It isn't even so hot here. Though her cheeks burn.

— You shouldn't have gone, says Melva. I told you not to go.

Worriedly, looking beyond Roberta.

— If they don't hurry up, Sir will be back and then they'll get caught.

> — I am passing down the valley that they say is so lone;
> But I find that all the pathway is with flowers overgrown.
> 'Tis is to me the Vale of Beulah, 'tis a beautiful way.
> For the Saviour walks beside me, my companion each day.

Walking along the long, lone way to school, with the smell of the bracken hot under the sun and with everything quiet except for an occasional crackle of twigs, the small explosion of a seed pod, or the cry and clatter of a bird; or standing, terrified, as the scrub cattle stampede over the blackened sticks left from last year's bushfire: listening, listening to the huge silence, Roberta sings the snake-frightening, cattle-scaring, God-calling hymn, her voice channelled along the walls of tall, inward-curving scrub or radiating out, a protective pool of human sound across the open spaces.

You could make as much noise as you liked — a whisper, or a shout at the top of your voice, it was all the same — and, after the impact, after the listening to it, the way it got lost out there across the scrub and into the watchful sky, all would again be still, waiting like a tensed beast.

— Vale of Beulah, Vale of Beulah, thou art precious to me.
    For the lovely land of Canaan in the distance I see.

Yet, on the way home, tired, she sometimes lay on the sand of the sand track and felt its warmth press against her (even when you dug your hands into the sand it was still hot; then, quite deep, it got cool), but not staying long enough for the bush to forget her presence, the bush creatures to too fully resume their stealthy busyness.

Lying so, peering through the scrub, she sees one day in a small clearing a black snake sleeping off a meal of half-grown rabbit (animal shape discernible under the shining skin). Trembling, barely daring to move, she gets to her feet, tiptoes a few steps, then runs until she is breathless.

Dear Berta (the first letter from Dorothy; Dorothy's aeroplane writing zooming above and below the lines), how are you getting on? I live at Geelong now with Mr and Mrs Bennett that I call Aunty Louise and Uncle Harry. They bought me a doll's pram and a doll and a new hat and coat and everything. Do you like living on an island I can see the sea where I live. Geelong is a nice place. I've got a pink satin quilt on my bed with a kewpie doll in the middle. Aunty Louise and Uncle Harry asked Mum and Dad if they can keep me and Mum said I arnt allowed to keep the doll's pram. There's a snapshot of me Uncle Harry took with his camera. I wished that I had a snapshot of you Berta. I remain your ever-loving sister Dorothy.

Roberta peers at Dorothy's long, lolly-curls, Dorothy's solemn, pretty little face; the new hat; the doll's pram. Dorothy's hand neatly bent at the wrist, upon the handle; Dorothy's immaculate shoes and socks; Dorothy, serene, seated on a wicker chair in a trim garden, behind her the brick and bay windows of a substantial house.

She must be living with the toffs.

Roberta looks in the mirror: her hair is dull and hard because Aunt Em says it ruins it to wash it too often; her wiry curls are tied back with a shoelace. She sees there the same solemnity as in Dorothy's pictured face.

She's sad, like me.

Perhaps she will never see Dorothy again; not see any of them again. She might be an orphan. She might be an orphan even now, and not know.

She cries, hard. Aunt Em opens the door. And Roberta shrinks away right inside herself. Aunt Em seeing.

– Why is my little girl crying? There, I said to Arthur they should never have sent that snapshot. There, pet lamb, don't cry. There now, have a good blow.

– Come on, lovey dear, you can help me plait my hair.

Against the wall by the door is the school library, a cupboard with double wooden doors which are kept locked except on Wednesday afternoons between two and four.

The children gaze at the shelves as if the open doors were secret panels, the books' presence forgotten other days of the week, their revelation a recurring disquiet.

With a few pages read without enjoyment, the books are returned to the cupboard at the end of the reading period. The children move haphazardly from one title to another, earlier selections forgotten, with books begun and rarely finished.

Then Roberta said please, she wanted a book to read; and it wasn't Wednesday or even two o'clock. They are packing up for home time, and they stop and look from Roberta to Mr Jeremiah.

– Sir's soft. He won't do anything.

– Tomorrow, says Mr Jeremiah. Reading period is tomorrow.

– Please, Mr Jeremiah, could I have a book to take home and read, please. I haven't got anything to read, sir.

Now she is scarlet, sick with the sense of her cheek.

– It's the cuts she'll get, not a book.

They stare at the new girl who doesn't know the rules. Books stay in the library cupboard and nowhere else, except maybe a picture book or a Bible or some not-to-be-touched treasure of your parents.

Yes, well why not? He remembers very well why not: they'd take the books away and forget to bring them back. Or they'd bring them back, after months, and say they "hadn't had the time", or they "couldn't get into" them. The set reading period was easier. Otherwise he'd be chasing up books forever more — not that it mattered that much, except that the inspector would want to know . . .

Read a lot of books himself, once; real books.

— Yes, well why not? Anyone else want to take a book home?

So every day is library day. Roberta begins at Alcott, Louisa May, and reads through to Wells, H.G. She reads at lunch times and on the way to and from school and in the evenings and has to be driven out to play. They call her a bookworm and laugh indulgently, pleased with the novelty of the word, as if they'd invented it. They tell her her eyes will drop out, that she'll be blind before she's twenty. She reads with more desperate haste.

Dumas; the Brothers Grimm; Ethel M. Turner's in sequence (a family ever dressed in white in a white house with everything white, even the flowers in the garden white; enchanting, then at last, absurd); Dickens to weep and sigh over, in pity and boredom; Mary Grant Bruce; *Billabong; Jim and Wally; Wings over Billabong; Back to Billabong; Westward Ho! Hereward the Wake.* Weeping, with Hereward's bloody head in her lap. *The Last of the Mohicans. Deerslayer. Eric, or Little by Little.* Dutifully shocked by Eric's dissipation, yet, was Eric so very bad? Was he not — dare she admit it? — most likeable when he was most wicked? *A Splendid Cousin.* Noble, good cousin: self-sacrificing . . . long-suffering . . . and yet . . . and yet . . . yes, a fool of a cousin.

The Thrall of Lief the Lucky. Her prize, her treasure, her own book to read over and over and know the beginning and the end and whole pages, chapters, by heart.

Helga-Roberta, the beautiful and adored, journeying in the brave Viking ship o'er unknown and perilous seas to the land of milk and honey. Heroic warriors, rude of manner as befits fighting men, became gentle, protective, courtly in her presence. Occasional lapses she smilingly forgave. Though fierce in battle, they were as children at heart.

Aunt Em, exasperated, slaps her for saying "by Thor" and "by Wotan"; it's not exactly swearing, says Aunt Em, but it's un-Christian.

– Please, sir, I've got nothing to read.

Mr Jeremiah looks at her, then looks away, and says nothing. After a few moments, when she thought he must have forgotten that she'd said anything, he says crossly.

– Well, *I* can't help it, can I?

He hardly ever got angry, and never with her. She was surprised and hurt, and said no more, but began reading yet again those books she had liked best.

You Are My Sunshine

Ruby Langford

I was born on Australia Day, the twenty-sixth of January
1934, at Box Ridge, Coraki, on the far north coast of New
South Wales. It was a reserve or Aboriginal mission. My father was a log-cutter and later he drove trucks carting logs
out of the Taloome scrub.

Dad was a tall and proud man, a family man, and he
watched after my mother. They were married when I was six
months old and my mother was sixteen.

A year later we moved to Stoney Gully mission near Kyogle, where Dad worked as a handyman for the manager. Sister Gwen was born when I was two.

In the afternoons Dad sat four or five of us on Bonnie, the
mission horse, and we took her to the creek. One of the older
kids sang "My Bonnie Lies over the Ocean". In the mornings
Dad hitched a slide behind the horse and went under the culvert to the dairy for milk cans and delivered them to the mission houses.

The houses were four-roomed, no lining, open fire for
cooking, and the windows were wooden slats that you prop
open with a stick. Mum looked after old man Ord, whom we
called nyathung. I sat on the step and watched his grey beard
moving as he talked, he was telling me stories in Bundjalung.
Sometimes he sang.

One night I was woken by movement in the room. I opened
my eyes slowly to sounds coming from a mattress in the corner. It was my mother moaning. Other women were with her,
shapes near the hurricane lamp. One of them noticed me
awake. She turned me over and covered me up. "Go
ngudam," she said, but I rolled over and watched. It sounded

nyathung − grandfather
Go ngudam − sleep

like my mother was hurt. In a while I saw them holding up a baby and heard the new cry. Then I went back to sleep. I forgot I had seen this, and forty years later the memory came back.

After sister Rita was born I started at the schoolhouse. It was on a hill overlooking the mission. There was a railway track and a culvert we went under to get to school. Our chickens laid eggs in the long bladegrass which grew everywhere. Old folk hunted for bandicoot and bunning in this grass. Dad also grew corn and pumpkin.

One day he came in with a gramophone so tall I had to stand on a chair to wind it. We played country and western records. I was about to climb on the chair one afternoon when Mum told me to come into Grandfather Ord's back room. He was lying quiet on the bed. "Go and kiss grandfather goodbye, he's going away." I leaned over and kissed his cold head. The men came and wrapped him in a tarp and took him out. I didn't know where he was going, I sat under the verandah and cried. Later Grandfather's son, Uncle Ernie Ord, came to stay.

We left Stoney Gully and went to live on the bank of the Richmond River outside Casino. We rented a wooden house on the Lismore Road. Uncle Ernie Ord and my father must surely have wanted boys in the family, Santa always brought us boys' toys. We never got dolls and prams, instead we would get rubber daggers, cricket bats, wind-up motorbikes.

I started school again. My mother took me by the short cut along the riverbank. She came half way, to a place called the Bamboos, and met me there after school.

The teacher's name was Miss Pie, and she taught us to sing. When I went on messages to the other teachers I'd give my message and sing a song. One day, it had been raining for a week, I sang songs about the rain.

That day, when I was walking home, the river was pretty high. I got as far as the Bamboos, carrying my lunch pail, and my mother wasn't there. I went on by myself, in and out of

bunning – porcupine (echidna)

the trees and staying on the track. A slippery sensation, and I was in the river.

I reached out but there was nothing to grab on to, the current sucked me under and when I came up I was out in the river. I took a breath. The current took me under again forcing the lunch pail out of my hand and I could hear a strange soothing music ringing in my ears. The river rushed me back near the bank and this time I grabbed a willow branch and hung on tight. It swept me in and I grabbed the reeds on the bank and pulled myself up. I sat there shaking.

Further up there was a fall in the river and I could hear it roaring. I climbed up the bank and ran hard, in my head the music and the water roaring.

My mother was making mulberry pies and my father was out in the scrub. I had a bath and calmed down. The Olives came over, Mrs Olive with her hair in a bun and one of the kids dragging a chaff bag he'd found in the bush. Mrs Olive went inside and the kids sat me on the chaff bag so they could drag me up and down the verandah. I got a big splinter in my bundung and my mother had me down on the bed cutting it out with a razor blade. The Olive kids' faces appeared at the window and I could hear them laughing as I yelled.

Uncle Ernie Ord had made a three-pronged spear for catching mullet. "Come on," he said one afternoon, "I'll show you how to catch fish. See this piece of string?" He reached into his pocket and laid some string on the table. He tied a bent pin to it. "Now you try." Then we made dough for bait and went to the fishing hole. Uncle Ernie threw some dough on the water and we could see schools of garfish and mullet rising. We came home with about six mullet — "a good feed", Uncle Ernie said.

A few nights later he almost used his three-prong spear on our neighbour, Eddie Webb, whom he heard on the verandah. When Dad came home and wanted an explanation, Eddie said he'd just called in to get some tea and sugar.

We didn't know it then, but Eddie Webb was sneaking after Mum. "Nyaiwayni bumanyi," Dad said, and Eddie cleared off.

bundung — bum
Nyaiwanyi bumanyi — I'll hit you

After that we moved back to the mission at Coraki. Much later I realised we were moving away from Eddie Webb, that his visits were more important than we thought.

One morning I heard a noise outside and went out to see a tall man on a horse riding into the mission. This was my Grandfather Sam, Dad's father. At this time I was a grumpy and pouty child and I wouldn't talk. Grandfather was a fine horseman. He hoisted me on to his seventeen hands high stock horse, Kangaroo, and I soon yelled out, "Get me down Poppy, get me down." He came into the house loping and bandy-legged from riding and sat down with my mother. He'd been away droving – Coraki, Dairy Flat, Kyogle. He stayed till Dad and Uncle Ernie came in from their log-cutting job a few days later and then he went away on Kangaroo. After he left, the men talked about cricket games they'd seen him play, how he was known as the Bungawalbyn Crack and could bowl anyone out. I didn't take much notice at the time, I was more interested in why Mum was so upset and quiet all the time.

There were days when she seemed happy and other times when she seemed to be waiting for something to happen. We now had a new baby brother, George. Dad and Uncle Ernie hardly ever came home.

It was a pitch dark night. I could hear Mum moving around in the room, talking in a low voice to the baby. I saw her wrap him up in a blanket and then I called out, "Mum, where are you going?" "I'll be back," she said.

I went to the door and watched her walking down the track to the gate. In the darkness the only thing you could see was the light on the top of a taxi. She got into the car. We didn't know where she'd gone, though I looked out for her and kept thinking she'd be back.

I was six, Gwen was four, Rita was two. The Breckenridges had got word to Dad and he came in a borrowed car and took us out into the scrub. Uncle Ernie was with him. They were like brothers, always wrestling and shaping up and biffing each other good-naturedly. We lived in a tent and played around the camp all day. Uncle Ernie boiled corned beef in a big boiler on the open fire, and cooked damper in the ashes. When Dad came into the camp at night I asked a few times, "Where's Mum?" and he said, "She's gone. She won't be back."

The days were hot and clear. Uncle Ernie had a tom-axe in his belt and a beer bottle with water in it. "Let's go for a walk, see if we can get some bush tucker," he said. He rolled his trouser leg up. We headed off into the scrub, big timber all around us; we could hear the axes ringing from where Dad and the others were, further up. Not far into the scrub Uncle Ernie pointed high up in a tree. At first I couldn't see it. He squatted down next to me and pointed again, and there it was. A big old grey bugger, goanna. "Watch this," he said.

He took the tom-axe and threw it hard. It landed in the back of the goanna's head with a thunk, and there was a silence, and then the goanna fell down right near our feet. Then next thing he had it on the hot coals back at the camp, and when it was cooked he offered some to us, but we wouldn't eat it. I remember the flesh was white like fish.

The next day he fed us on boiled swan's eggs. Half a one was enough for each person. Later he gave us cobra, worm-like things that were embedded in waterlogged willows in the Richmond River.

Later on we moved back to Box Ridge. As you came through the main gate of the mission there was a church and then, in the shape of a square, a school and about ten houses. This was our place, this was where the Kooris lived, about fifty of us. We stayed with some people called Breckenridge. In the middle of the square was a tennis court.

Out the back was Uncle Ernie's hut, which he'd made from a few pieces of galvanised iron and hessian bags, with a single bed in it and his tin trunk with all his belongings. There was a fire bucket too. To keep warm he sat in front of the fire bucket and told us stories about bush animals: binging, jarahny, guyahny, burbi, also kangaroos, cranes, emus, possums.

binging – turtles
jarahny – frogs
guyahny – possums
burbi – bear

He started to doze and we poked him in his big belly and woke him up. He went on with the story. One night he told me my totem was the willy wagtail. Years later I think about that small bird. I am a very large woman with a bird singing inside me, good news and bad.

Uncle Ernie was an Aboriginal clever man, that is, he knew magic. When Mrs Breckenridge got sick and didn't seem to be getting any better, Uncle Ernie was sent for. I watched him go to his tin trunk and take out an old tobacco tin where he kept the hair of his dead father. He warmed it on the fire bucket by rubbing his hands together.

Then he went back inside, and hunted everyone out of the sick room. I looked through the window and I saw him put his hand with the hair on it to her forehead. He sang and chanted in the lingo and stayed there for about an hour. When he came out he told us to be quiet, she was sleeping. She slept for a few hours and then she got up and set about doing her work.

A few months later an old lady came to visit. Uncle Ernie told her that he was asleep one night in his shack and he heard his dead father's voice calling him to wake up. When he did he saw a hole in the hessian bag around his hut, and he knew someone was watching him. He sneaked around the back in the dark and saw a man walking away towards the bush. He followed and the man disappeared in front of him.

We all ate in the kitchen of the house. It was my job to do the washing up and pack the table. The cups were made of jam tins or Sunshine Milk tins, which were called pannikins. One night Uncle Ernie was sitting at one end of the table and he said, "Do you want to see that pannikin move up here? Watch this." He waved his hand towards himself and the pannikin moved across the table and stopped right in front of him. We looked under the table to see if he had strings tied to it, but there were no strings. "How did you do that?" we said, and he laughed, and his whole body shook.

The headmistress at the school was Mrs Hiscock. She taught us to cook, sew and grow vegetables in the schoolyard.

Every Monday morning we were given a big tablespoon of sulphur and molasses to clean our systems out. Behind the school was a field of millet belonging to Mr Breckenridge, who was a broom maker. One day Rita fell on a squaring axe and needed about ten stitches, but they didn't take her to a doctor. They bathed us in the water that had been used to wash the linen, with handfuls of caustic soda added. Did she want us to go white? Instead we had burning skin.

To get from the mission to the town of Coraki you went across a common where the cows were kept. In wet weather the common turned into a swamp. On the other side of the swamp was a gate, a shop where the Kooris went, then the town. In the main street, which ran parallel to the river, was a baker with a crow in a cage on the counter. When the baker was out the back, the crow called out, "There's blackfellers in the shop!" Further up the street was the Masonic Hall where we went to the pictures: Hopalong Cassidy, Tom Mix, Charlie Chaplin. Only a few times we went in to the pictures – three miles – the adults piggybacking kids home after. The pictures had segregated seating, one side for us, the other side for the whites. At the hospital they had special wards for Kooris down the back.

One afternoon I was sent to stoke the fire. It was down to coals so I put chips on and brambles and fanned it with a piece of cardboard. It still wasn't lit so I poured kero on and the rings were still on top and it blew up in my face with a loud boom. I was in pain for weeks, I had no eyebrows and all my face was blistered. They didn't take me to the doctor.

Not longer after this some kind person must have got word to Dad about the way we were being treated. He came in the truck and packed our things. Uncle Ernie was the only one who knew we weren't coming back. He helped us into the truck and kissed us goodbye then walked away from us with his head down crying.

It was a long ride from the mission at Cooraki to Dad's brother's place. Bonalbo was a small town nestled in dairy hills, and we were to stay here for the next four years. Uncle Sam came out to the verandah to meet us, and took us inside to meet eight or nine other relatives who lived there. Dad stayed a few days, and then went back to the Taloome scrub, timber cutting. We settled in and went to school.

Aunt Nell was a big woman who wore an apron with pockets where she kept clothespegs and a pencil and notepad for the shopping list. From the cowbales where I was milking I could pick up the drifting smells of suet pastry, steak and kidney pie, the warm sweet smell of stew. In winter we came in from school and squatted on the woodbox near the stove. There was a fountain of water always boiling, and a tap at the bottom for making tea.

The house was the original station house, on a property eight miles long. Aunt Nell was a Hinnett, and the house was left to her family by the original owners, who the Hinnetts had worked for.

Aunt Nell had a daughter before she married Uncle Sam. Her name was Shirley (Midge). She was two years older than me and she washed our faces and combed our hair and put ribbons in it. I was nine years old.

Dad was away all week and came home at weekends. We watched for the lights of his truck coming around the hills outside town; we swarmed all over him as soon as he arrived. We jostled to see who'd get to sit on his knees first. The two little ones always managed to beat me.

When the job cut out, Dad went to Sydney to find work. He left us in the care of Uncle Sam and Aunt Nell and then we only saw him at Christmas time. He sent money to Aunt Nell for our keep.

Uncle Sam and Aunty Nell always referred to each other as mother and father. She was ten years older than him but it didn't matter to them at all. They were the best parents we could have had, and I promised myself if I ever had kids I'd never leave them.

Eventually there were nine people at the table.

At tea time Midge and we three sat on a long stool, the others had their own chairs. Uncle Sam at one end, Aunty Nell at the other. Aunty Nell's sister Aunty Flo and her brother Uncle Willy on one side and their nephew John on the other. Later Aunty Nell had a baby girl, Judy.

At mealtimes only the grown-ups could speak and make conversation. The kids cleaned the table when the meal was finished, then we did our homework by candlelight. There was a big lamp which Aunt Nell kept in her bedroom at night. Their room was next to ours, and she checked us in the night to see if we were covered properly. It was very cold in winter.

We did our chores before we went to school. My job was to milk three or four cows before breakfast. I separated the milk by hand, so by the weekend I had a big bowl of cream in the icebox. Then I'd make butter for the next week. It was the days of the Second World War – sugar, tea and butter were rationed. Gwen's job was to polish the dining-room table. One morning Aunty Nell came in and said, "Put some elbow grease into that!" I was going through from the milking to get dressed for school. When I came into the kitchen I found Gwen on all fours looking into a cupboard. "What are you doing?" I said. She was looking for the elbow grease.

The twenty-five-pound flour bags Aunt Nell bought were washed and boiled and then cut up to make our pants. She made our dresses and hats from starched cheesecloth. It was my job to damp the starched clothing down and I hated doing it. When I was called to do some chore I shinnied up the crepe myrtle outside our bedroom and hid in the leaves. Uncle Sam called me the Big Noise because when I wasn't hiding I was singing as loud as I could.

When I stopped, I heard chooks making their small noises, pecking around in the vegetable garden and under the fruit trees. Down near the cowbales were two orange trees and a big mulberry tree. There was also a passionfruit vine growing in a cow pat, and at the side of the house a grapevine. It was an old weatherboard house with rafters in the kitchen.

At the back of the house was a big paddock with suckers in amongst the gum trees. I went down to the biggest tree and climbed up. You had to watch out for spitfires, grubs that sting. At the end of the paddock was a fence; then the stock route. On sale days I watched cattle coming down here like a river, heard the calls of the Indian cowboys, the Khan brothers, who lived up the back.

From this tree I could see the whole town – Marty Askew's shop, the hardware, the feed and grain store, Jim McQueen's butcher shop. Behind the hotel were the cattle saleyards, the butter factory, the track to the swimming hole. Soon I knew who lived in every house that I could see.

Aunty Nell was having a baking day. From the cowbales, or the creek, or up the tree I could smell the cakes cooking. When I went to the back door I saw Uncle Sam palming a few cup cakes. He hobbled out and handed them to us. Soon Aunt Nell said, "Father, where're all those cakes gone to?" "I don't know," he said, "must be fairies taking them." As soon as we heard this, we ran like blazes, leaving him to take the blame.

He had a gammy leg and when we asked him how it was stiff and why, this was his story. He said when he was younger he was a horse-breaker and the horse threw him and he was a flying angel.

Later we found out he'd had polio. It never stopped him from playing cricket and working on the Shire Council. He was a grader driver for twenty years. He liked to dance around the kitchen imitating how we danced with our boyfriends. "Look at how Gwennie dances with Cippi Hannan," and he threw his gammy leg out and danced in the big kitchen. Once he stuck oranges down his flannel shirt and walked around like Betty Stubbins. He half-limped half-danced towards us. "Look out," he said, "these bosoms'll knock your eyes out. Specially when you're comin' round the corner."

The people in the town were friendly, there was no prejudice against us. It felt different from the atmosphere in Coraki. We went to Sunday School and church, we sang at concerts and church festivals. At the festival we bought a watermelon for sixpence and there was enough to go around eight people. The harvest festival was held when the corn was in. We were getting the church ready. Uncle Willy was the gardener at our place, and he brought in squash and marrows. The farm people came in with sacks of corn and put them all around the church walls. In a little room at the back the women unwrapped home-made cakes and put the urns on to boil. Mrs Bull arrived with the draughthorse and sulky. The Browns and the Grays came in their utes with pumpkins the size of watermelons, grey-white skin, and sweet and dry inside. We called them cow pumpkins. I was presented by the Bishop of Grafton with a prayerbook and a scroll, which Aunt Nell hung in the dining room.

After the harvest festival we went to the nearest farm, about six hundred yards from the town, Mac McQueen's place. We showed him the chaff bag and asked if we could have some corn for the cookout. We had fried corn, fricasseed corn and then corn fritters. In the end Aunt Nell was pouring castor oil down our throats.

A couple of days before Christmas we were sitting on the back steps watching through the suckers of the trees. We saw the bus pull in at Marty Askew's shop, we saw Dad, tall, coming across the footbridge towards the church. We ran down to meet him. He had one suitcase slung on his shoulder and one down beside him. We knew the suitcases were packed with things for us, clothes and toys and bags of nuts for the Christmas table.

We opened our presents at the same time, and the family watched. We started with the biggest parcels first. Pale blue skirts and blouses to match with sailor suit collars, packets of scented soaps and talcum powder, crackling presents that opened up to be lollies and licorice, and then the last ones, tiny combs and mirrors.

When we were quiet again, Gwen went over amd stood near Dad's knee. "When you're away so long," she said, "what are you doing all the time?" Dad said he drove a bulldozer. "What's a bulldozer?" she said. Rita looked up from her presents and said, "Oh Gwen, don't be silly. Don't you know it's a bull that dozes."

The next morning I was in the kitchen and Dad sent me to get his shaving gear out of his suitcase. I opened the lid and lifted up some clothes and there was a photograph of a beautiful lady in a big white picture hat sitting on a chair. I stared at the photo and then turned it over. The words said *You are my Sunshine, love Evelyn.*

Dad came in with a towel around his neck and said, "Haven't you found my shaving gear yet?" When he saw the photo I said, "Is that our mother."

"Yes," he said.

I stared at the picture. "Isn't she beautiful," I said.

"Yes," he said. "She's very beautiful." He closed the lid of the suitcase.

A Good Rexona Town

Ian Moffitt

"When you go," said my father in 1949, sipping his cocoa, staring into the gas fire, the safety pin fastening the neck of his striped pyjamas, "When you go, I s'pose I'll be a lonely old feller."

"Don't go to Turkey," warned my mother, who lay in bed each night, feeling the top of her head lift off with worry. "They're a horrible dirty race." And my young sister Ruth explained brightly, "You'll get a knife in you." And added to the others, "I suppose he'll come back in the same shirt he goes in."

Our family's little plateau of provincial glory lay behind us. We had descended to the city from the North Coast of New South Wales; death and distance were about to scatter us for ever. It was not an important family, of course; just another middle-class Australian home which had honoured God and the king, in its (C of E) way. And yet it represents, to me, that whole anaesthetised Australian society: like silkworms deep in the mulberry leaves, we were spinning myths for today's radioactive winds to sweep away.

Someone — I've forgotten who it was — told me once that he was wandering home from school one afternoon during the Depression when he kicked a ball into a trench. One of the workmen looked up, and he found himself gazing down into the face of his father. "Don't tell your mother," his father said and — because his family, like mine, was obviously white collar (the father donning old clothes after he left the house) — the melodrama of that old encounter impressed me vividly. *Our* Depression, as children, was not so dramatic: my father worked as a clerk in the old New South Wales Government Savings Bank in Sydney; kept chooks, and grew fruit and vegetables. I remember only the tail-end of it all: those gentle, beaten men at the back door, who offered mothballs from thin, cracked cases while we willed our mothers to buy.

My father Syd was small, but he never seemed so to me when I was a child. He was born on a dairy farm down the South Coast of New South Wales; a skinny fellow with a long Irish face and such large ears that his brothers and sisters used to jump out from behind a corner of the farmhouse holding saucers against their heads, to mock him. He had to go to Sydney to earn his white collar, and he wore it always with irritation: first as a bank clerk there, later as a bank manager up the North Coast at Taree. His mother was a Roman Catholic (the daughter, we did not discover until 1983, of an Irish Catholic convict, Edward Mitchell, transported for fourteen years, in 1828, for deserting from the 65th Regiment of Foot). His father was a big C of E bushman of Irish Protestant stock who used to gallop after her on his black horse whenever she tried to whip the buggy-load of kids into town for the local priest to baptise. My father used to chiack her gently, in later life, as she prepared for Mass — "What have you got to confess, Mother? What have you ever done?" — and she always replied, "Oh, don't be silly, Syd," and, when pressed, "Well, you can have wicked thoughts." That really delighted him; he used to throw back his head and roar laughing. We children, like him, never took organised religion too seriously.

We lived first at Wahroonga, on Sydney's North Shore, when a six-pounds-a-week clerk, with five children, could own a home there. It was a cream Spanish-style bungalow with green shutters on a big corner block with tall gums, and my father spent two years building a small chookhouse (with spirit level) down the back. He posed proudly for a photograph before it; now a red-brick house sits like a slab of raw liver in that yard where we played dirt cricket.

The artistic Lindsays were neighbours then, and Charles Kingsford-Smith strode up Coonanbarra Road each morning with a cheery wave, on his way to death (in 1935) in the Bay of Bengal. But our heroes (Bradman & Co. apart) were mainly English (and Scottish); British history drenched all our dreaming. A rich kid and I used to sail his lead Scottish soldiers in a bush pond at the end of the street; I remember slinking back one morning to sift the mud for wounded Highlanders he had forgotten. Finding them was magical: like uncovering golden potatoes for the first time in rich black earth, or eggs in long grass laid by slow-strutting fowls.

On Saturdays we played cricket in Wahroonga Park, where we happily allowed dogs to hug our legs, unaware, while adults stalked past with cold faces from the train. I heard my first joke there. "Well stopped by A. Box!" cried Frankie Mussett when the ball struck a packing case in the grass, and I thought that was immensely clever — Frankie became a dentist. And on Sunday after church we straggled on bushwalks, with sticks stuck in our socks to protect our legs from magpies; yearning week after week for a green tissue kite which had caught like a dream in the top branches of a mighty gum. It seemed to be the promise of life, that kite: the magic, the excitement, far beyond our reach in the Antipodes.

One night my father brought home the world in a cardboard box, and we tried to guess what was in it. A beehive? He unwrapped, instead, a small Radiolette mantel wireless to supplement his (private) crystal set, and inside this little glowing city — behind its tiny oiled-silk facade — Robinson Crusoe strode each week along the golden shores of his island while we clustered in awe. My father still lay on his bed, listening to his crystal set with a handkerchief over his eyes, but the standard of living was rising gradually. He bought my mother a washing machine too, and she crushed her hand so badly in the wringer that my elder brother gave her twopence-halfpenny wrapped in a green tea coupon for the doctor, and promised to take her to Jerusalem when his feet touched the bottom of his cot. My mother never did get to Jerusalem, of course: parents were there to assuage *our* wounds. I can still remember pressing my face into my father's overcoat as he piggy-backed me home from the dentist.

I was eight when we moved to the North Coast. "Welcome to Taree, a Good Rexona Town", proclaimed a faded wooden sign on the town's outskirts, with "Farewell to Taree, a Good Rexona Town", on the other side. Between that welcome and farewell lay eleven years in the new Rural Bank in the main street, a building considered so splendid that the local *Manning River Times* published two columns of minute description of its interior. It was huge, two-storey, red-brick, with a painted lead coat of arms, "Orta Recens Quam Pura Nites", shining high on a front balcony above the banking chamber. This faced the rambling, lacy old School of Arts opposite, and its residential rear sat on a rise above the broad Manning River, which was sullen mostly, but swirled chocolate-brown in flood-time over our back fence, sweeping torn trees and bloated cattle down to the Pacific Ocean. On one side of the bank was a vacant allotment, on the other solicitors' chambers, with our concrete car drive sloping between. Our father did not have a car; we kids hung a heavy punching bag in the garage, and once wheedled our small sister's girlfriend into performing a clumsy dance in there without pants. Over in Europe, the Hitler Youth had higher aims.

Our childhood there was pretty typical of Australian country town life before and during the war — only the names differ. We observed the fiction that we were all equal, but the social tiers in the community were as plain as the growth-rings in the logs at the sawmill. We had second-rank status, it became apparent: just behind the leading doctor, but certainly ahead of the high-school teachers and clergymen and lesser banks; certainly ahead of the proprietors of department stores and hardware shops and Roman Catholic publicans named Bede O'Something-or-other (who were "Licensed to Sell Fermented and Spirituous Liquors"). The Bedes were as far beyond our ken as the Catholic kids who gathered in medieval seclusion behind the high red walls of the local convent. We were modest members of the Anglican establishment, attending state schools, and state schools had absolutely no contact with the Catholics — the fault of both sides. Roman Catholics, to us, were potential traitors; how could they worship King and Empire when they pledged even higher allegiance to an Italian Pope? It seemed a fatal chink in the sacred armour of patriotism.

Sunday mornings in Anglican homes — the radios booming hymns from St Andrew's Cathedral in Sydney — were unutterably miserable. Unlike the Catholics, we had no built-in compulsion to attend or shrivel in hellfire. Each Sunday therefore, we hung around in a sort of Anglican purgatory; perhaps if we crept around quietly, our mothers might forget to send us to morning communion. Some of our elders called the worthy local clergyman Tubby, and their lack of respect lowered ours; a dark halo hung around his head, and we coldly observed that the edge of his mouth was wet. He bustled into the hotels sometimes, laughing nervously as he drummed up donations, but the gossips bestowed on him a darker design. He therefore blocked our view of the Mount; although it was wrong of us to take the small-town talk of the grown-ups so literally.

The town's leading families believed they were egalitarian, but they used white working-class girls in the town as cheap maids, and black girls from Purfleet, the Aboriginal mission station over the river. The Aboriginal men drifted into town to swig cheap wine in sodden, hopeless groups in the mangroves down by the river, or to huddle in a section of the front stalls roped off for them at the Boomerang Theatre on Saturday afternoons: the melting rainbow-curtain unfolding tales of justice, ironically, to us all. And once a year the townsfolk drove out to Purfleet for the annual corroboree: painted, puffy half-castes shuffling through the tattered fragments of their Dreamtime, with hand-out rations bouncing in their bellies while we pattered politely with our applause. It was apartheid, but we did not know it then.

We C of E learned, very quickly, to resist the central core of the Christian message. The regimental banners around the altar told us to do so, and so did the hallowed Union Jacks, and (a little less important) the Australian flags. Reverence for Christ lay like white, Christmas cake icing over the adoration of war: crack its pious plea for peace, and below we found what really mattered — the rich dark depths of nobility and bloodshed, of heroism and manhood and individual suffering. The clergyman placed his big fat Bible on the golden eagle and preached platitudes we had forgotten by the time we filed from our pews, but we did not forget those flags. If we were lucky, a second war might thunder, and call us to a higher state of being than Sunday Christianity could provide.

Anazac was our God then, in the country towns and city suburbs; here we sought our noblest expression, our truest identity. Gallipoli and France formed a leaden sky which brushed low over the towns and parks where we played in the thirties, and this infected our innocence more than the antique horrors in *Cole's Funny Picture Book*. Dimly we became aware of death. The Second War failed, really, to overlay the awakening consciousness of that first conflict: the blue-yellow tones of Tobruk, New Guinea's garish green, smeared but lightly the awful sickening grey of the First Great War — the splintered trees and shell-pocked mud, the corpses in craters, and long lines of little men trudging on duckboards to the Front. Middle-generation Australians grew up amid this memory; clambering around captured World War One cannon in the parks (or rusted machine-guns in the villages), touching the maidenhair fern flourishing in the pitted digger helmets, reverently registering the gassed uncle coughing in the next room.

We studied oval photographs in albums ('Bertie, Killed on the Somme'); sang hymns on hot, cracked asphalt to teachers gathered in the shade; revered the "Menin Gate at Midnight" rising above school sport trophies in the hall. And on holidays, if we were lucky, we haunted the Australian War Memorial in Canberra, where on drear days, dark as the Dyson drawings inside, we inspected death sealed under glass: the bullet-pierced water bottles, a punctured felt hat, some rusted improvised bombs, a muddy moneybelt dropped on a sortie from Quinn's Post. The mortars sat around us in vapid, round-mouthed astonishment; soldiers ran through a mute barrage of tiny dioramas (Pozières, Lone Pine); a crushed Australian bugle picked up on Gallipoli lay dully with the torn shoulder-straps and badges, a broken, busted bayonet, some boxes of spent ammunition. Soon, it seemed certain, we'd find something of ourselves. Only look long enough amid the half-known names, Passchendaele, Fleurbaix, and there might be your own. Somewhere beneath the tattered shoulder-badges, the broken bayonet, a birth . . .

The Anzac March in those days was our only valid festival. The First World War was our first birth, our second but a

mark in a register. The old Diggers spun the two-up coins in
streets sharp with rosemary, and we stood with no doubt, no
doubt at all, amid the jangling medals and clashing bands, the
rainbow ribbons of watered silk. Red-eyed women, granite
soldiers bowed over rifles, golden letters on marble cakes
fixed to monuments: these were what mattered. We stood together against the Yellow Peril and the Cruel Hun, not *for* the
defeated black army on our doorstep; we were the Christian
Crusaders hacking a path to glory. Allan Ashbolt spelled it
out once in an address at Sydney's Anglican Moore Theolog-
ical College: "We were brought up to believe that war was a
kind of initiation into manhood, that without the personal experience of combat, of trying to kill someone who was trying
to kill you, we would be less than men. The test of a man was
whether he fired a shot in anger."

Meanwhile, we fired shots at rabbits and, lacking more
meaningful trophies, killed black snakes and hung them over
fences. We were very badly informed, of course: the immediate perimeters of thought in our town encircled the cemetery,
the long, lonely Pacific beaches which lay beyond the river
(and where we searched for wreckage from the world beyond), and the golf course. The golf pro always seemed to be
a spicy, handsome city man: a sort of junior trainee Satan's
apprentice, tanned and handsome, who masterfully gripped
the wrists (and perhaps more) of the townsfolk's sporty
daughters. But the schizophrenia of our isolation sank deeper
than this.

We lived in a lush coastal dairy district – rode bikes in it,
sailed and surfed and swam off its shores and in its creeks –
but we believed (when our teachers told us) that ours was a
harsh sunburnt land. We never *loved* it, as the English cherish
their land; we were exiles in the wings of a secondary stage,
Australia; if English history was green and blood-red, ours
was burnt black and off-white, a fibrous root dangling beneath the rich foliage Back Home. So we loved England,
then, and (with mocking reservations) admired America. The
dairy paddocks, the mangrove swamps, the ghostly
ringbarked gums outside our doors: this was alien country.
We roamed, more truly, with Tim Tyler and Buck Rogers;

brushed aside the lawyer vines in damp green jungles in our brains; scrambled up the high, pitiless rocks on the North-west Frontier; pelted forward with the Scots on veldt and pock-marked Passchendaele, awaiting the call which never came.

Our education system, not the Japanese, betrayed us; our inherited race-memory stunted our growth, not masturbation. Fantasy was our only escape from the country's oppressive monotony: *Champion* and *Triumph* and *Film Fun Weekly* were our touchstones (measured out, one story a day, for the week); we yearned for starfish and buckets and breakwaters and Pop and Grub on pebbly beaches 12,000 miles from our golden sand. English meadows drenched with English history, English swords buried beneath English acorns, English battleships and fighter planes and Billy Bunters: they all sat up there on a shining ledge beside our lean bronzed Australian Anzac. The desecration of a church was an idea which we instantly rejected, but to desecrate England with doubt — that never occurred to us.

The heart of the Empire beat in London; we sat down in the bum — in, but only just, and grateful for any morsel which slid down to us.

It was comforting, and harmless, in a way. We murdered Shakespeare at school and worshipped his body (cutting him into dry little pieces; peeling open each word); admired Elizabeth I (nobody told us about her syphilitic sores); sentimentalised with Dickens, who shot through on his own kids. "When Brit-ain fir-ir-ir-ir-irst at Heav'ns co-ho-mand": there was an incredible rightness and glory as we sang about it all, which old Australians still swallow. *The Child's History of England,* the Union Jack, Arthur Mee's *Children's Encyclopaedia,* the *Boys' Own* paper — the defeats were more glorious than the victories; even Horatio, holding the bridge, displayed excellent British pluck for a Roman. We charged with the Light Brigade; we held the Thin Red Line; we first pondered the inevitability of death in that fort with Beau Geste (surely there could have been *somewhere* to hide?). Ours was the last inspired, soul-stirred generation before the Union Jack shrank to a Carnaby Street ash tray, and the hot pink

ebbed from the map – the last to stand so nobly, and so
betrayed, with Buchan and Biggles against those niggers and
dagos and wops. The Lordly Ones, we were, 12,000 miles
from the action, fighting secretly for our ancestors' heritage
and suffering psychic wounds which persisted for decades.

And yet this land became a part of us. For me, its splintered, moonlit paddocks lie always in the brain; the wide
bends of its western rivers flow through my veins; its bush, to
me, is always, for some reason, myself – bristling and
whispering my waiting death. But love, no. That seemed,
even as a child, a word for softer lands like England, and for
more rounded human beings, a word which our politicians
mouthed in peace time, but which was valid for our poets only
in war. Nothing was ever ours, and we knew it then: our
gaolers had stolen it from the Aborigines, and tossed it to us
by default. We parroted patriotism, but it was not for our
land. Not for Taree.

Of course, it wasn't a noble stage of life for us. The city
reached us only by taxi each holiday weekend, when outside
in the grey dawn in the gutter I waited for my elder sisters,
Geneva and Marjorie, to sweep down from the railway station – home from their Sydney office jobs for three days,
their rich perfumes (as they bundled out of the back seat)
spicing our awareness of the delights beyond. Onanism, pre-
Portnoy, was all that really scared us then – through war and
drought, flood and bushfire, it was the only trauma which
haunted us while empires rose and fell abroad. Sex dragged
slow circles around our little minds, like rats with their back
legs squashed: our evil thoughts doomed us to eternal damnation. We resisted, of course, as best we could. Once, crying
"Get behind me, Satan!", I swung around to punch a scaly
devil leering astern and struck my brother, who had been
sneaking up for more innocent mischief. But sex lay all
around: not temptingly, as in today's full page magazine
nudes, but amid, God help us, the creaky corset ads in the old
David Jones catalogues from Sydney. And it lay in sinister sil-
very piles in the linen press outside our bathroom door: fuzzy-
haired Hollywood heroines swaying in Arabian palaces in the

silent screen magazines, their nipples burning darkly beneath the gauze.

Knowledge of evil lay, for us Anglicans, not in a sermon (the Catholics were way ahead of us there), but perhaps in a jolly boy at the school who masturbated publicly, or in a musty thriller over in the School of Arts (where the ruddy, sensible English detective was actually the murderer). The boys used to gather in the schoolyard to share, obliquely, their guilt and fear. "They reckon someone would say, 'that you get hair on your hand . . .'" And all would swing in wild glee on some dull farm boy caught uncurling his palm under the empty blue sky, as if surreptitiously reading the notes inked there for a music exam. The farm boys got back at us with tales of half-animals, half-humans, glimpsed on their properties; we were never *quite* sure they were wrong.

Sex, like murder, was unsavoury: we pored over divorce stories in the Sydney *Truth* ("Whence came the aroma of an expensive perfume that permeated the medico's Morris coupe?"), and studied photographs of ramshackle cars discovered on stock routes, nosed into scrub, or abandoned in sewerage-grey Melbourne suburbs, with "Body Found Here" in a box-with-arrow. The big whisper at school then was that a woman was no virgin if her buttocks wobbled when she walked, and many was the unfortunate office-girl we trailed down the main street, blackening her blameless reputation with this infallible sex-detector. Good sensible black bloomers sent us tottering from the basketball pickets with our hearts thudding, and the soft flesh inside a teacher's knee drove us into the transports of damnation (it was still a time, after all, when mothers frowned at daughters who sat awkwardly in living rooms). The depth of ambition was to see a girl's pants: more, if possible. One school friend used to wait until his elder sisters (home from university with their girlfriends) were undressing, and then fling open their bedroom door dramatically. "Saw *you*!" he would shout, pointing as they jackknifed. "Saw *you*! Saw *you*!" I bumped into him years later in the city, and joshed him about such memory and hurried away, fearful that his impressive career was in sudden jeopardy. He did better than that, actually: once, with complete absorption, he coloured his penis with red and blue ink in class, making a gay little man of it. The girls whispered, pointed and elbowed each other, but he did not notice: very achievement-oriented, he was, in whatever he undertook, and extremely short-sighted.

Damnation in hell was easy to believe, eternity in heaven more difficult: we knew we could never earn such an honour. I found my own answer, not in church, but in the drear, soot-smeared paddocks beyond the railway station, where we played school cricket on cracked, concrete pitches. Yellowing old newspapers used to blow there — catching in a bush, fluttering on to the next — and that seemed to me the only limited "Eternity" I could accept: we were caught in one human memory after we died, trapped momentarily in the next, before we all blew off the playing field forever. I should, as captain, have been concentrating on the game, but I could never stand up against fast bowling anyway. I suspected, privately, that I had been made captain because I was modest and polite to my teachers, and because my father had solid standing in the town, but said nothing, of course.

We were the silent generation: we rebelled *sotto voce*. I dreamed of thundering through the hills with the bushrangers but, in fact, portrayed the person in the winning Bridal Set at the Juvenile Ball. I redeemed my shame, in part, by also winning the Lucky Spot. While executing an awkward One Step with another boy in the Belmore Hall, I fell on the slippery floor under the selected Spot on the ceiling. Lying there, with a nose-bleed, I heard the compere hail my victory.

The war came at last, and the *Sydney Morning Herald* stamped in official with a formal notice amid its Births, Deaths and Marriages and its old In Memoriams and new Engagements. "Outbreak of War: It is hereby notified for general information that war has broken out between Great Britain and Germany. Dated this third day of September, 1939. Robert G. Menzies, Prime Minister." The men of the BEF were about to die for democracy and Danzig; the German war machine, its treads mucky with blood, had crunched over a little man with a winged collar, a broken brolly, and an apologetic smile. "The dual wave radio of your dreams!"

shouted the advertisements in the Sydney newspapers. "What's Happening in Europe as it Happens DIRECT!"

It was a tense week, of course: the BBC voices rising and fading, as if in the far wash of the waves; the newspapers publishing optimistic despatches: "The Polish Soldier − Born Fighter . . . A New Role for the Cavalry". The ABC actually broke into a religious service in Melbourne with Chamberlain's announcement, and Menzies assured us that truth was with us in the battle, truth was our companion on this journey.

The trouble was, *we* kids weren't going on any journey: the smoke billowing up from Poland was, for us, little more than a major industrial disaster in another state. "The old Digger will not be found wanting," declared an RSL official, but we were too young to be young Diggers; the war maps ("shaded areas indicate countries which are neutral so far") did not include Taree. The country was still treating its peace-time corns and bunions, its backache, kidney trouble and rupture worries with Hutuwai Tonic (pronounced Hoo-Too-wy); with Bidomak, the Tonic of the Century; with Horlicks, which guarded against night starvation ("Wife thinks: 'It breaks my heart to see him slump down night after night . . .' BUT LATER"). Later, for us, pray God, meant our fair share in the glorious bloodshed.

Meantime we had more immediate preoccupations: it was certainly going to be rather a heavy year, as a September 3 astrology chart ventured, but Ralph Richardson might come to the Boomerang in *Clouds over Europe* ("A glorious spoof"), and Ron Richards had just outpointed America's Ossie Stewart, the world's Number Three middleweight, in Sydney. Personal violence, anyway, was closer to our hearts.

We staged our own duels with .BB guns in the Flanders landscapes of ringbarked paddocks, and with boxing gloves in our backyard above the river. My father had been a delicate young man − too poor-eyed for slaughter on the Somme − but he had bequeathed his interest in boxing to my brother and me: a barbarous sport, in a way, a poor man's chess, but certainly, it seemed to us, Man, Life, an ultimate affirmation of masculinity. He used to "talk" a very good fight to us in imaginative additions to our mother's letters ("P.S. I ended nearly all my fights while my opponents were up in the air. I lifted them off their feet with the left, and hit them on the button as they came down. Dad"). But his spectator interest was certainly genuine. He had danced off his stool in the old Government Savings Bank, "menacing" his patient mates: "Come on. I'll smother you with science. You'll think it's raining boxing gloves." He had clung to crowded trams crawling down from King's Cross to the old Sydney Stadium to see Darcy and Griffo and Fritz Holland and Eddie McGoorty — I can still hear his nasal bush drawl of those names. He had chuckled for decades after hearing a man roar "Sit down, rat's breath!" at a fellow spectator peacocking around at ringside.

We absorbed this as reverently as his readings of Henry Lawson (he chose Lawson as my middle name), and we reinforced it with annual pilgrimages to Sharman's boxing tent at the Taree Show. Fighters in silken robes banged the big drum, the spruiker shouted, "Step right up. Don't let the grass grow under your feet. What's your name, son? Where you from? Gloucester. Well, I'll tell you what I'll do, Gloucester", and we drank it all in through our eyes and ears — Australia's bullfight, a recurring symbol for some Antipodean Antonioni, the stuff of some future musical.

We sent away to Hughie Dwyer in Newcastle for boxing instruction sheets, which we treasured like the Dead Sea Scrolls, and memorised reverently for years: "To learn this scientific course, procure a bag, chaffbag, canvas kit bag or corn bag", training to have a go, when that was the height of national aspiration. (I can still see the magic brown envelopes emblazoned NEWCASTLE STADIUM, Australia in black, with Where They Fight! splashed beneath it in red.) Patiently, disapprovingly, our mother stitched dark maroon and silver shorts, with the initials on the right leg, and we bobbed and weaved as the Stukas screamed down on the AIF Sixth Division in Greece.

Paperbound collections of war poetry became my real bibles; my flesh crawled over John Quinn's and Tip Kelaher's verses, the more cultured muse of Rupert Brooke and Patrick

Hore-Ruthven. Quinn's *Argument*; Kelaher's *Ginger Mick* and *Wounded from Tobruk*; Hore-Ruthven's *To a Young Man Who Died*, and (though pre-war) *To Pamela on Exmoor*: they spoke to me over that ruffled grey Manning River at a time when war was honourable; their verses curled around the First World War monument in the main street. The town's first soldier, back from the Middle East, was a magical figure to me: his white hat band, his white webbing belt and puggarees proclaiming that he had been Away. I think they probably sent him straight back from Egypt, under-age.

The Japanese pushed the war closer; it was no longer merely a wavering fanfare on the wireless or a glorious black bulletin from Dunkirk. One morning the town kids woke to find an American Army truck convoy lying in the main street, and we wandered along it, registering the different accents from truck to olive-brown truck. There again we found ourselves at a disadvantage — we seemed to have only educated and broad accents — but at least our men were lean and brown and hard, and these were soft and white and puffy. And we still had Right and Honour and Manhood. We made plans to take the hills with .22 rifles if the Japanese invaded, and my father vowed to shoot my young sister with the bank revolver rather than let the Japs get her. My main Freudian desire then was to cover a retreating column with a machine-gun at the top of a pass in New Guinea (preferably from a giant mock boulder in which I could shelter in perfect — well, almost perfect — safety. I had not forgotten Beau Geste.) Sometimes we saw Italian POWs in plum-red uniforms passing through by train, but they did not really count (though even then, beneath our fashionable dismissals of their prowess, beneath the derisory stories of perfumed officers in ladies corsets etc., we sensed the gentle humanity of ordinary men). We never did see any Japanese, but we added little buck-toothed soldiers with giant sabres and two-toed sneakers to our artistic galleries of Hitlers and Goerings and Goebells. My cousin died in a fighter off New Guinea, but I did not notice at the time. "Rat-tat-tat-tat-tat," I was reading. "Rockfist Rogan, RAF, zoomed his Spitfire in a steep dive at enemy territory." My young sister, Ruth, who was more practical, became an aircraft spotter at night.

London might be sheltering in the Tube, but our social life then was pretty intense. "Goin' down the street Fridee night?" we'd ask each other unnecessarily. "Yair. You?" "Yair." Friday night was late shopping night, and we youths dressed up and walked down Victoria Street. We never bought anything, except, perhaps, a milkshake at Zaunder's cafe, but we savoured what warmth we could from the lit shops, the bustle of the department stores, the clusters of adults chatting outside the banks and cafes — vaguely aware of the shadows of Aborigines hanging around down the dark sidestreets near the river with their wine bottles. They existed almost beyond the edges of my consciousness then, like those flicking shapes you catch in the corner of your eye which disappear when you turn your head. I wrote my first published short story (highly sentimental) about one of them for a national collection in the forties; the editors hailed it as "an unusually discerning study of a half-caste." It was discerning all right: I had never spoken to an Aboriginal in my life.

I didn't even speak to the bush lairs, for that matter. The bush lairs then wore clean shirts (no ties), with the collars turned up around their necks, and baggy trousers with wide bands studded with a console battery of buttons. Sometimes my father stopped near them on the hotel corner, took out his handkerchief, and absently blew his nose. "Wait here," he'd say. "We might see a fight in a minute." It was as if, for our elders, fights never ended with fractured skulls on the pavement; brawling was a harmless pursuit of manhood, like shooting 'roos and ringbarking paddocks. No conscience seemed to curse our elders then, as it does us now; no namby-pamby awareness of ensuing suffering. Drunks were comic or disgusting, but never, it seemed, in danger of their lives.

My brother Paul was much bolder than I was. He and the dentist's son lashed together iron-bar bombs, filled with potassium chlorate and sulphur, and hurled one while the dentist, who worked nearby, was drilling the local sergeant of police. The dentist had to push the sergeant back in the chair,

claiming a car backfire: he knew that if the elder Moffitt boy
was tossing bombs, his son was there tossing them too. My
brother could fight like a threshing machine; he battled the
bush lairs while I was memorising their trouser buttons; he
was a bit frightened of the Aborigines, so naturally fought
them to show that he wasn't. But he liked the Aboriginal kids,
and sometimes played Rugby League against them ("At half-
time they'd all go off and their bloody fathers would come on
and kick shit out of us.") He loved every minute of his country boyhood; he was out after the local girls while I was writing odes. His best friend used to upstage him by taking a girl,
whom they were both pursuing, to the pictures in his father's
Whippet. But Paul was waiting in her linen-press when his
mate farewelled her, gallantly, at the front door.

There was no threat from the war. We roamed the streets
heaving rocks on roofs during a lone brown-out, but the only
dangerous troops were Australians: they pursued our big sisters when on leave from a nearby camp. My father, however,
testily refused an employee a rise while England fought with
her back to the wall — it was no time, we comprehended, for
Self — and my mother worked day and night for the Boys.
Her 1941 diary bore evidence in her large pencilled hand of
her patriotism. "Greek Card Party; VAD Bridge Party; Mrs
Kerle's Afternoon; Matron's Bridge; Red X; Red X; Red X."
There were diversions, of course (Pictures tonight,
"Charlie's Aunt"). But behind the cards and the Mah Jong we
knew that the massive troopships were sliding out where sub-
marines lurked, and that the *Repulse* and the *Prince of Wales*
had gone down, drowning soldiers like ants (and how could
we make a victory out of that?). The women over in the
School of Arts sewed up thousands of calico parcels for the
troops and made nearly two thousand camouflage nets at the
leading doctor's home. My brother joined the AIF (and could
not eat for several days in the mess, so unskilled were his new
companions at table), but my mother sent him food parcels to
Darwin, where, as a signalman, he monitored messages from
Japanese bombers. She was, we knew, the best cook in town:
inside her blue cookery book, with "Recipes" inscribed in
gold script, were glorious dishes with her own judgments

added: Passionfruit Jelly (special), Fig Conserve (good), which was an understatement ("Fill cake with bananas, passionfruit and strawberries and whipped cream . . ."). She made Peaches: biscuits filled with jam, brushed pink with cochineal, and arranged amid real peach leaves. She made Afghan Biscuits, dark with cocoa, iced with chocolate, a jaunty walnut on top of each one. And she made Kisses and Uncle Toby's Biscuits and Melting Moments, and icecream (studded with granules of gelatine). And she cooked rainbow cakes for birthdays, and Russian pies and pumpkin scones and savoury eggs and stuffed celery boats and prawn cocktails (good). She created for us, in short, while we longed only to destroy. A strong woman, square and brown and righteous (shushing my father's bawdy little songs), who taught us to respect and like women by her example. We valued only one offering she did not provide: an icecream cake every Christmas from the icecream factory, studded with melting pink daisies.

There wasn't much excitement. The grocer, taking orders at the kitchen door, was a big event. The dented metal cover of his order book fascinated me, the way he carefully inserted the carbon paper, scribbled the list. One day I touched my first aeroplane out at Old Bar 'Drome: a Gypsy Moth with WELCOME TIBBETT painted on the underside of its wings. It must have flown over the ship which bore him to Sydney in the thirties. Another day I fondled the gleaming railway lines out in the bush from Taree, the magic track stretching up to Brisbane, down to Sydney, which one day would bear me away into the world. I fired the bank revolver once into a stump, and I loved the smell and weight of a .22 rifle in my hand, but the squeals of wounded rabbits scrabbling away into the bushes soon depressed me. I wanted to kill only enemy soldiers. Heaving rocks was as anti-social as we went: one night another boy and I rose silently before a glittering light-bulb sign advertising a visiting circus, "Barton's Follies"; we hurled the rocks into the facade and fled with sober faces back into the bosoms of our families.

I secretly feared Siberian wolves under the bed, and though I did not tell anyone, I opened closed suitcases to prevent evil spirits hiding in them. But the only real dangers were a shark or a stingray in the surf, an oyster or rusty jam tin on the rocks, a submerged snag in the river, and a burning foot on a back tyre if the bike's brakes failed. We played Rugby League against Newcastle and Kempsey, and prized sporting praise in the *Manning River Times* or the *Northern Champion* more than respectable placings in examinations. We even won our Bronze medallions for surf-lifesaving. What a bitter little initiation into Australian manhood that was. I had drilled till then only in a local hall, paying out the line as the beltman trotted directly ahead to the horizon (which happened to be the main door of the hall). But a strong rip was running when we got to the beach on the day of the test, and the beltman dashed, not straight into the waves, but fifty yards up the sand to allow for it. I remember staring straight ahead, unaware that I was permitted to turn with him, while the rope burned through my hands, and the blood dripped down in front of my eyes.

Not to surf, not to enjoy the beach, was heresy. Each Christmas we took a beach cottage, the black sand glinting in the bare backyard around the privy, the pitiless sun forcing me to squint as I crouched for photographs to record the holiday. Monotony oppressed me: sometimes a school of sharks cut through the Pacific beyond the breakers, and I longed for escape, longed to crack the carapace of adolescence; longed for love and adventure to burst above like a starshell, exalting me, enriching me, with new meaning, with glory. I escaped, I suppose; I joined the Sydney *Sun*.

The Day That Lasted Forever

Peter Skrzynecki

Our life at 10 Mary Street began nearly four years earlier when we arrived in Sydney; before that we lived in a Migrant Holding Centre, or camp, for two years in Parkes, in the central west of New South Wales. These were the very early years in Australia's post-World War Two history in which many new nationalities arrived in large numbers from Europe.

We disembarked from the *General Blanchford* on 11 November 1949, and were taken to a camp on the Lime Kilns Road outside Bathurst. The camp was built mainly of Nissen or "igloo" huts — long, semicircular sheds of corrugated iron, set among khaki-coloured hills. I always thought that was a good colour for those hills: we had come to Australia because of a war, war meant soldiers, soldiers meant uniforms — often khaki in colour. It was a dopy idea, but maybe these hills would protect our lives in this new land just as soldiers protected a country from the enemy. My memories of Bathurst are almost non-existent, except for the long dust road through the hills — and for the fact that it was there, in that camp, that I saw a naked woman for the first time. Today, only two months from my tenth birthday, I get embarrassed and shy when I think about it. I never tell anybody, even when I hear older boys at school giggle and laugh when they describe what a woman looks like "in the nuddy". I just listen, feeling strange all through my body, and I think that my face must be burning with shame at what I know already. Of course I had to tell it in Confession before I made my First Holy Communion. When the priest said that I must remove impure thoughts from my mind, I replied, "Yes, Father", even though I wasn't sure if I'd had any impure thoughts.

The incident seemed very natural at the time — the result of curiosity and daring.

The showerblock at the Bathurst camp was made of corrugated iron and there were small holes in some places. When the group of boys that I associated with discovered these, we used to sneak down in the dark when we knew that women were having their showers, and spy through the holes.

One night we were caught! Whether someone had heard or seen us — or maybe somebody had reported us — we were caught. A woman screamed (throwing water at the wall where we had glued our eyes). Other women swore and covered themselves. Men suddenly appeared from out of the darkness and caught us by the necks, cuffing our ears and laughing as they did: enjoying themselves at our expense. The women threatened to tell our mothers straight away. We escaped into the night, hiding wherever we could. "Let them tell," the older boys jeered. One of them, a tall Latvian boy named Peteris, who had a very strong voice, laughed so loudly I thought he would wake the whole camp. He was five or six years older than most of us. Peteris became a hero in the eyes of the younger children who admired anyone who could be so defiant in the face of a beating.

That incident in Bathurst aside, Parkes is the place in the country that has left the most vivid and lasting memories. Those two years were among the happiest times of my life — even when I compare them to the days in Mary Street. Parkes represents to me everything that Australia stands for as a country: the people, the land and its wealth, the wildlife and the extremes of climate — fields of wheat, sheep in open paddocks or huddled in a flock under a huge gum tree, cattle, galahs clanging and wheeling over a farm and its homestead with willows or peppercorn trees, grain sheds and tractors . . . and a road of red dust and stones cutting through it all — east to west, straight through, a road that led to Sydney and the outside world that I would travel on and never expect to return.

The two years at Parkes were spent in the expectation of leaving one day, though my parents never knew exactly when that would happen. It all had to do with money and opportunity, just as it had to do with making a future for themselves and myself in this new country, as it did with forgetting what they had to leave behind in Europe and what World War Two did to their homelands. I heard that phrase over and over, when I was expected to hear it and when I wasn't, that one day they would own their own home; that they would leave these "barracks" and one day the future would be bright for everyone. Australia could make everyone's dreams come true if only they were prepared to work hard and save their money. Thrift was a virtue, and that was a reward in itself.

My father left the camp and travelled to Sydney where he found work with the Water Board as a pipe layer. He was a member of a "road gang" and would be located in a different part of Sydney every few months, mostly in the newer, developing suburbs like Bankstown and Liverpool. He lived in a place called Tent City at the Water Board's depot at Potts Hill, at the back of Regents Park, between Birrong and Brunker Road, Yagoona. Every month he would visit my mother and me at the camp, stay a few days and return by train. For children like me this was the most thrilling time; the day before the train arrived from Sydney, we talked about nothing except what we thought (and hoped) our presents would be. These ranged from boxes of chocolates, felt toys, comics, Meccano sets, scooters, tricycles or bicycles, spinning tops, games like Snakes and Ladders, Ludo or Dominoes, boxes of coloured pencils – anything that arrived from that magical place called Sydney: so far away from the dusty roads, galahs and hot weather that we equated with the countryside around the camp – and with a distance that could have been to the moon or Mars. Two hundred miles was the length of eternity when all you had was a pair of feet to travel it.

Parkes railway station consisted of one platform with a wide roof arching over it, supported by long steel curved frames; it was both a terminus and a junction where passengers used to change for the Condobolin and Broken Hill lines. As you stood on the platform and looked east or west, it presented what I thought must have been one of the loneliest sights in the world. Although the edge of the town lay just behind it and in front, sidings with shining criss-cross lines cut across the sleepers and blue metal. Grain would be spilt from freight trains along the tracks and on the grasses that grew along them. Standing on the edge of the platform you had the view of an unreachable horizon confronting you, a landscape that shimmered in the heat, almost bare – just like you had when standing on the red-dust road that ran in front of the camp.

The railway lines stretched, silver and metallic-hard, from one distance to another. Joining one world to the next. And there, on the edge of a cold grey platform (almost frosted in winter, icy like the rails) I held my mother's hand and waited for my father's arrival, for the first glimpse of smoke on the horizon that meant the train had come into sight and soon my waiting would be over. Sometimes I remembered the promises my parents made about leaving Parkes for ever and travelling to Sydney – to live in the home they were going to buy. That was a sensible idea, I thought. Then they could grow all the flowers and vegetables they always talked about. We would have chickens and ducklings and I would get to see them hatching from eggs – something I had wanted to learn about. A pet dog, also. That was a promise I *would* hold my parents to. In the meantime, Parkes was my home; and even though I disliked the food queues in the dining hall and how crowded it sometimes became around the rows of barracks, I enjoyed the life that was mine for two years. I had playmates of my own age, of nationalities that were similar to mine; we argued and fought, but we also played and attended classes in the school inside the camp. Some of the best times occurred when our fathers came on their visits. While the adults sat around and ate, played cards and sang, we played with our new toys – with pop guns and wind-up toys, marbles and dolls: all or any of those wonderful toys that we had waited for so excitedly. In the evenings and into the nights, as thick clouds of cigarette smoke filled the barracks, we read comics and fell asleep behind a wall of voices, dreaming under those pitch-black skies and golden specks of stars, ignorant of the time when any of us might have to leave the camp with our families. We were just happy that our fathers had returned.

Once, when my father arrived, I learnt something about

him that I never knew. His present to me was a white bi-plane, a Tiger Mother made entirely out of wood, without a single nail. Every piece of wood had either been glued or fit-ted together like a jigsaw puzzle; he even painted a red, white and blue RAAF "bullseye" on the wingtips. The propeller spun in the wind when I ran along and held it up. What seemed most wonderful of all were the wheels. Carved from wood! And two little cockpits! My father had spent months of his spare time in Sydney carving and building this surprise. When he gave it to me, a neighbour from one of the huts snapped a photo of three of us standing under an enormous gum tree, its twin trunks peeling and splitting, bark fallen at our feet. My father was dressed casually and stood with one foot forward, holding a cigarette; my mother wore a long dress and a wide-brimmed straw hat; I held the Tiger Moth at my side and stood to attention, like a soldier, squinting at the sun.

The camp itself was a former RAAF Central Flying School whose facilities had been converted marginally into living quarters for over one thousand immigrants. The gates were opened in 1949, when it officially became the Parkes Migrant Holding Centre. It had a school, a hospital, a post office, a din-ing hall and was made to appear as much as possible like a small township. The "real" shops were in Clarinda Street, Parkes — the main street that cut the town in two like a wide river, or a long hall running through a big house where front and back doors had been left open and you could see straight through, end to end, as if there were no doors at all. That was where my mother took me shopping for new clothes, for ice-creams and lollies and any "extras" that we needed for our hut and weren't able to get at the camp.

For most of the two years we lived on the town's outskirts, my mother worked as a domestic for several families in town itself, including that of the mayor, Mr C.J. Barber, whose house was in Gapp Street. A long stone and brick building with high verandahs, it was the most impressive house I had ever seen. Neat lawns and beautiful front and back gardens surrounded Number 6. It was just like pictures I've seen since of the Botanic Gardens in Sydney. The shrubs and trees were quite extraordinary, considering they were in a part of New South Wales that was very hot and dry in summer.

My mother took me with her to Gapp Street on one occasion and didn't leave me to be minded at the camp. That was a treat at any time, as I loved going into town on the bus and looking out the window at the passing countryside. The driver used to say that one day the road would be sealed and there would be no more red dust to fly up and get into our noses. People laughed. No one believed him. The bus squeaked and rattled as it jolted everyone over bumps and pot-holes. There was a barrier at the main gates of the camp that had to be raised and lowered whenever a vehicle left or arrived. Once the barrier was brought down and the bus turned right on to the main road towards town, anyone who was worried or had a problem changed in spirit or attitude. Children looked forward to a day in town the most – to the possibility of strawberry icecream in cones or getting a new pair of shoes or a new coat. Adults had the opportunity of mixing with the locals, with the townspeople and farmers in for the day from their farms.

But the day that I arrived in Gapp Street, one of Mr Barber's grandsons, Allan, was there also. He and I were to be playmates for the day, despite the fact that my grasp of English was very poor and I still depended on sign language. That was a surprise for both of us: him with his long yellow locks and freckled face, me with my short black hair and olive features.

Disaster, straight away, when I was told that it was his birthday and his grandmother produced his present, a toy carpentry set: hammer, saw, chisel, rule, pencil and some nails. What a lucky boy! I started to bawl when he wouldn't let me play with it – and continued after his grandmother persuaded him to allow me to share it. And when it was time to return home, I refused. Again, because of the carpentry set. I didn't want to leave the house in Gapp Street. We'd had a cake for Allan, as well as lollies and cordial. I wanted to bring him back to the camp with us or else for me to stay there for the night. In the end, I left, crying, as I was led out of the yard. Mr and Mrs Barber waved to me. They were good-natured people, kind, with a patience about them that seemed to belong to the land itself: as if they knew that everything would work itself out, following the pattern of a season. Mr Barber used to say that there would be plenty of work in Parkes for everyone: "the dinky-di Aussies and the New Australians."

After dinner that night my mother and I went for a walk around the camp. The night sounds of crickets and other insects followed us and echoed through the darkness. Noises crept down from the trees. Soft, rustling whispers. Frogs in the distance, creating a chorus of their own, probably at a creek or dam. Stars twinkled as tiny jewels and the Milky Way streamed overhead like it was about to pour stardust across the whole sleeping world.

My mother made a reference to my earlier behaviour. "You must behave yourself. Don't be jealous."

"But I want a toy set like Allan's got."

"Not now."

"Why?"

"I can't afford it. Not at this time."

"When?"

She shrugged her shoulders. "Maybe when your father returns from Sydney. But that's not what I want you to learn."

"I don't want to learn. I just want a toy carpentry set like Allan's got."

"That's exactly what I want you to learn."

"What?"

"That you can't always have what you want."

I was angry with my mother. When she spoke like that I knew that she was being wise; but I wasn't interested in learning to be wise. I just wanted what I wanted.

"Mum!"

"Look at the stars," she said calmly. "Where I grew up on a farm in the Ukraine, we had mountains called the Carpathians . . . the stars were even brighter than they are here. We were poor. Sometimes we cried because there wasn't enough food to eat. Yes, we cried. But we also knew how to laugh . . . and we learnt to go without . . . We survived all that, and the war." She started to hum and sing very softly as we headed back to our hut, away from the forest and the empty space of the airfield.

The open fields looked like they were a part of the moon. I imagined a small plane like my Tiger Moth droning over the hills, coming in to land, silver light reflecting off its wings, spinning off the propeller as it slowed down, the pilot waving from the cockpit; but the moonlight was shining through him, creating a ghostly picture.

Whatever the lesson had meant to teach me, I knew it was over when my mother began to dream about her homeland. I knew that she missed it, but I never, never, understood her homesickness; nor did I know at the time that she and my father would have returned to Europe the next day if it weren't for me. They believed that my future was here in Australia, not back among the ruins of Europe where the smoke of war was still rising from the ashes created by dropped bombs.

Next day I was invited back to Gapp Street as a treat, on the condition I promised to behave myself, whether Allan was there or not. I promised, though I couldn't be sure of the results of my promise if Allan was sitting on the lawn, smiling, or carrying around his carpentry set.

Before we entered the house through the back door, as we always did, Mr Barber came out, followed by his wife who was holding Allan's hand. I stood back, suspiciously, holding my mother's hand. Why were they smiling? In the sunlight that shone through those trees and beautiful flowers, the day was about to affect my life forever.

Allan held out a wrapped present for me from behind his back. Even before I struggled to mumble "Thank you", there were tears swelling in my eyes. Tears of joy, of embarrassment, of wanting to run away and hide from yesterday. I could see how surprised my mother was and thanked the Barbers over and over. Allan took my hand and off we went into the backyard − bubbling with excitement, our minds full of ideas about all the things we were going to build. My last memory of Allan's grandparents was the expression of kindness in their faces: they seemed to understand what being a small child was all about − much more than the child himself who refused to listen to his mother the night before and thought his whole world had collapsed.

That day has lived in my mind as one of the brightest and happiest I've ever had; it was just like the other morning on the way to school when Danny Fussell stopped me and I had to lie about my sandwiches because I thought he was going to steal them. Then that exhilarating moment when he left – as I hurried off to school, hearing the sparrows and peewits behind me, face into the rising sun, and feeling as though I'd walked through it and become a part of it for ever. Maybe that day in Gapp Street was a part of that morning too – and tomorrow will be a part of it, and the next day and the next.

I wonder where my little friend the bird was on that morning I met Danny Fussell or on the morning in Gapp Street? What would it be saying if it was here? (Maybe it *is* here!). Keeping quiet as it often does. Watching, head cocked to one side. Looking ahead like a little old wise man. Saying nothing. Sometimes I wonder where it lived in Parkes – in the barracks and managed to keep out of sight, or in the old Air Force hangars and sheds? Or maybe down around the sewage works? When it first appeared on the ship coming through the Great Australian Bight, I thought it would visit more often, but it never did. Not like now, since we moved to Mary Street.

All my friends would think I was weird if I spoke to them about it, so why should I? How do you explain something that appears and disappears in dreams?

My parents have said they will never return to Parkes – that they've had enough of food queues and waiting at railway stations, just as they say they will never return to Europe. They swear that the sea voyage was their last journey. There is a note of resignation in their voices when they speak like that, not sadness. I think that they have learnt some kind of powerful lesson about life – like my dreams – that cannot be explained to others because it means different things to different people. Parkes lay at the end of that voyage, and their time at Parkes had come to an end. They knew that after two years they must move on. After we left, I heard them repeat many times that they had no desire to return.

But not me.

Living those two years in Parkes meant all those things to me, as well, but on a different scale. Where my parents remembered Europe vividly, I had only broken pictures of it in my mind: of rabbits that we kept for meat in a Displaced Persons Camp in Germany; of snow falling outside a window and a veil of filmy whiteness covering the ground and sky as far as I could see; of travelling by train through dark pine forests that filtered sunlight and hid the scattered remains of bombers that had been shot down and were painted in camouflage colours; of boarding the *General Blanchford* at Naples — staring up at the huge gangplank — for the start of the voyage to Australia.

After a sea voyage of four weeks, Parkes meant open spaces, paddocks, sheep, cattle, gum trees, magpies stalking the ground on frosty mornings and throwing back their heads to sing. Parkes meant hot dry weather, a bushland that I loved walking through and picking at branches of wattle, or encountering the scent of eucalypts for the first time. Parkes was the countryside where I saw a wedge-tailed eagle strung on a gate of a property where my mother worked as a washerwoman; finding a flock of sheep huddled under trees in the heat and rubbing their woolly rumps against the trunks, leaving fleecy threads in the bark and their droppings covering the ground; or standing inside a slab-split hut on that property, lost in a maze of harnesses that hung on its walls, under its cobwebbed rafters; or getting thrown by a horse named Pig, so called because it liked to "root". Parkes is the origin of all these memories, as well as being the name of the township that gave its name to our first "home" in Australia.

Just as my parents remember vividly what happened to them in Germany during the war, so I can remember, at least in part, what happened to me in Parkes.

Just as I remember coming home from school one afternoon and sitting on the back steps, waiting for my parents to return from work — watching sparrows hop around the garden, along the rows of potatoes, listening to peewits calling to each other behind the fence in the bushes that grew around Duck Creek.

An unearthly feeling came over me, like I was about to fall asleep or become airborne into the afternoon light; yet I sat there, my knees drawn up under my chin, lost in a daydream. When I looked up I could see houses and factories on the hill that rises beyond Duck Creek and Jensen Oval, where Sefton ends and Chester Hill begins, where Virgil Avenue cuts the suburbs in half and dips over the horizon. A small boy ran across the scene and disappeared among the skeleton frames of buildings; he was fair-haired and freckled. Another small boy followed him, dark-haired and olive-skinned. Both were carrying toy hammers and saws, laughing happily as they ran off, disappearing among the unbuilt houses and into the khaki bushland shadows. For a moment, the sun blazed with a burst of brilliance as if it was morning, not late afternoon. I blinked, rubbing my eyes, staring in disbelief.

Black Sheep

Margaret Coombs

Many people congratulate me on my exquisite manners, forgetting of course that etiquette is the birthright of all Australians.

— Dame Edna Everage

The monologic must always be a construction . . . As soon as
I articulate "I", I have constructed an entity that is not me.

— Terry Threadgold

" 'Baa baa black sheep, have you any wool? Yes sir, yes sir,
three bags full.' " my grandmother sang. She stayed with us
often. She was my mother's mother, a widow, lived on the
pension. Nan was what I had to call her. Nan or Nanny.
Skinny Nanny was a knitter, forever trailing bags of wool,
had won prizes in the Royal Easter Show in Sydney, had had
her work bought for sale by David Jones. She was a champion
knitter but she always liked to follow a pattern, never made
up her own, never even thought of it. " 'Yes sir, yes sir,' " she
sang. When the pattern was wrong, sleeves wouldn't fit
sleeve holes, which happened sometimes, there'd be drama.
Trunk calls would be made to the Paton's knitting adviser to
demand that the problem be sorted out. Outrage would fill
the house. Nan was the daughter of a house builder, her
mother's work home duties. She'd married an engine fitter at
seventeen, had had three children by twenty-one. "One for
the Master and one for the Dame and one for the little boy
who lived down the lane." My mother had been the youngest,
the spoilt one, her sisters said. At twenty-one she'd married
Dad.

Nan nettled Dad. She insisted on listening to *Blue Hills* every
evening on the radio, however mortifying to the intellect my
father found it. Then she prattled on about the characters as

if they were real people, was elated by their triumphs,
wondered aloud what shade and length of frock they'd be
wearing to their weddings, wept when they moved to Perth
or died. Again and again my father expressed to my mother
his exasperation regarding Nan's ignorant behaviour, and my
mother tactfully conveyed this quirk of Dad's to Nan, tried to
persuade her to humour Isaac, to keep her speculations about
Blue Hills under her hat.

Nan took no notice. She had no great respect for my
father's opinions, having benefited from treatment by a sil-
ver-haired Macquarie Street specialist herself. She'd learnt
from *Blue Hills* what real doctors were supposed to be like,
and knew that her carnation-wearing Dr Guilfoyle was one of
them, and that compared to him my father was a dud. You'll
catch a cold standing in that draught, Isaac, she'd comment.
You ought to have a cardigan on. At other times she warned
that if he stood so close to the fire, chilblains would ensue. Re-
marks like these were apt to bring an apoplectic look to my
father's face.

My father was from a poor family, poor but clever. This was
what Nan didn't seem to understand. He was an honours
graduate in medicine and so was his sister. You're just like
Rachel, my mother would sometimes say to me when I irri-
tated her. That was all I knew about Auntie Rachel. I knew
more about Dad. His dissections of people's brains, done
when a student, were enshrined in glass cases in the Anat-
omy Museum at Sydney University. He'd taken me to see
them once: ghastly bloodless lumps lying sodden in the bottom of neatly labelled formalin-filled jars. I sometimes felt he
wished my mother would remind Nan of these achievements.
There were other facts Nan was never reminded of. In the
second year of his marriage, my father had left my mother
and her baby in Streaky Bay, the little town in South Australia where he'd first practised, and had worked his way to
England as a ship's doctor, planning to return with a higher
degree. By the time the ship arrived at Dover, my mother
realised she was pregnant again. My father turned around
and sailed straight back to her.

Later, having actually read *Mein Kampf*, my father had other reasons for his lack of eagerness to rush to Europe for a higher education, and instead had joined the army during the war. He'd learnt more surgery from reconstructing sick and wounded soldiers than he could have from swotting over text-books anyway, he said, though of course he didn't have a piece of paper saying that. It galled him to have to put up with Nan's panegyrics in praise of her Dr Guilfoyle with his silver hair and his FRCS. In a lowered voice he would proffer the opinion to my mother that Guilfoyle was a charlatan, that his treatment of Nan had been criminal in its excess, that Nan ought to be told, that she should take the rogue to court.

Nan was slightly deaf. "Baa, baa, black sheep," she would croon over her knitting, impervious as a canary to my father's silences, sighs, grunts and thunderous looks.

My father's favourite story about me from before I remember was when we'd all been driving somewhere in the car and I'd looked out the window and pointed at some animals and said, Moo-cows, moo-cows, and my father had said, Yes, but some people call those kinds of moo-cows sheep. He told this story often. I loved him to. I never tired of it. His voice would be warm and happy. He would laugh. His eyes would light up. He and I were in cahoots.

Black sheep, dark horse, my father was black-haired, brown-eyed, olive-skinned. My father was a Jew. He was not a proper Jew, not a Yiddish-speaking refugee from war-torn Europe but one born in Yerranderie, New South Wales, English-speaking, Henry-Lawson-quoting, anti-Zionist, thoroughly committed to calling Australia home. His father, too, was Australian-born, son of German-speaking Prussian-born Jews of no fixed occupation or address who'd arrived in Melbourne during the gold rush, were in theory immigrants, not refugees. His mother was called Anglo-Jewish – though she'd been brought to Sydney from Woolwich when she was two.

But I grew up quite unaware of any ethnic explanation for his personal eccentricities. Even at Christmas, I didn't catch on that what was odd about Dad that he was a Jew. I thought merely that the world was divided into Protestants and Roman Catholics, and that *all* anti-Roman Catholics were like us. Christmas for us meant Santa Claus, not St Nicholas. Christ wasn't mentioned. We retreated to paganism, we embraced consumerism, glad of how they served to paper over cultural cracks. Others might have a star at the top of their Christmas trees but we had a gorgeous cellophane-winged fairy in a pink net dress made by Nan — and a fairy we called her, not an angel. Our cards eschewed religious subjects, avoided even the word Christmas. We had ones saying, non-committally, Season's Greetings: plain for patients, and pine-tree-decorated or Santa-Claus-adorned for family friends. Seasoning's Greetings, Seasoning's Greetings, I used to chant. For us Christmas was unashamedly about being showered with presents and overstuffed with festive food. The solstices were spoken of. In the northern hemisphere it was the winter solstice and we Australians politely went along with celebrating that, even though it was the summer solstice here. We put cotton wool swabs from the consulting room on the Christmas tree to signify snow. For Christmas dinner we ate hot roast pork.

And thereby curls a tale. This was the one time of the year when we ate pork. My mother used to warn us playfully not to mention to my father that it was pork because, as she put it, Daddy doesn't *like* pork. She said to pretend that it was veal. Years later, when I finally met Auntie Rachel, I found out my father's father had disguised his un-Australian preference for kosher food by getting doctors to prescribe him a lifelong diet of vegetables and fish — which the whole family followed for the sake of his health. It was a diet that just happened to be kosher, yes, evading the whole issue of how meat should be prepared, but it was pursued, Rachel said, in the name not of religion but of Science. Well, Science was what we had instead of religion in our house in Narramundi too. That my father had accidentally been brought up on kosher food wasn't mentioned. My mother said that it was because he was a surgeon that he didn't much like meat of any kind.

She said he was apt to dissect, not carve, a roast. She said it would put anyone off. I thought of the bleached brains stagnating in their jars of formalin, and agreed. She said that on Christmas Day she'd cut the meat in the kitchen, would put plenty of gravy on my father's serving, and Daddy would never know the difference. Just this once, she always said.

Daddy did know, of course. He permitted it. This exhilarating game of pretending to trick my father was part of the joy of Christmas. To my mother and Nan and me, it was our carnival day, the day when the hierarchies that ordered our world were turned upside down and folly ruled.

But the pleasure of our ritualised rebellion was spoilt by my father's absence from the meal itself. He was never there to be seen to play at being deceived. On Christmas Day, Dad's patients got drunk, dropped saucepans of scalding water on themselves, cut off digits with carving knives, drowned in dams, got into murderous brawls, had catastrophic head-on collisions on the pothole-ridden dirt roads. I never heard the confidential details at the time, only heard the phone ring, heard soft, urgent voices, saw my father depart, my mother smile brightly at us like a shop assistant, saw my father slump back sallow-faced and exhausted some hours later, saw him force down his gravy-drowned pork, rewarmed over a simmering saucepan, swallowing it with the sort of grim determination you see on the faces of students in mock Iron Man contests shovelling down weetbix saturated with warm beer.

"Baa, baa, black sheep," my grandmother sang while he ploughed through his food, advised by my mother not to sing "Silent Night".

But it was my father who gave me the black sheep. Not for Christmas. It just appeared one day, was there in the backyard munching grass when I got back from school. I could see that Dad was very pleased with it, thought having a black sheep was a wonderful joke. His face was full of mischief, full of smiles. His eyes sparkled. He gave little laughs of glee. Helen's Baa Lamb, he said the sheep was called. It was mine.

At first I was frightened of Helen's Baa Lamb, so little did it resemble the representations of black sheep in picture books, the sheep that accompanied the words of the song Nan sang, the baa lambs that accompanied Little Bo Peeps. My sheep was too large, considerably bigger and heavier than I was, and yet at the same time not big enough to ride. It was no fun. It didn't do anything except stand around eating or else bolt full-tilt if you gave it a fright. It didn't frisk. It was a fat, stolid thing with a face rendered expressionless by the thick mask of matted wool that covered it. You couldn't see its eyes, so didn't know if it liked you or not. It had menacing hooves. It wasn't even properly black but had a small cloud of white on top of its head like a birthmark, and the end of its snout was white as if it had drunk from a can of whitewash, except for its pink albino's nose. To pat this unattractive animal was not a pleasure. There was something wrong with the feel of it. Its wool was too greasy, too coarse, not what you could imagine ever turning into the fine soft stuff Nan knitted with. Worst of all, it wasn't clean. Little clouds of flies buzzed perpetually around its orifices, drawing disturbing attention to its possession of a poo-hole, genitalia, eyeslits from which discharges emanated, a nose and mouth from which fly fodder dribbled and oozed.

We didn't have Helen's Baa Lamb for long. It disappeared as mysteriously and abruptly as it had arrived. One day I got home from school and found it wasn't there any more. That was that. My mother explained that Daddy had sent it back to the farm he'd got it from. Because it had become fly-blown, she said. Besides, she said, the lawn had become fly-blown too. My mother hadn't liked the mess the sheep made on the lawn, the little piles of pea-shaped shit that the flies loved so much. Nor had I. We lacked the facilities for keeping a black sheep, she pointed out. We couldn't cope with it. Real black sheep weren't quite as obliging as the black sheep in the song!

School was another world. The teachers were fools, my father implied, though he still always saved their lives when they got sick. Miss Pennicuick is the one I remember best. Miss Pennicuick was called the library teacher. She was tall and old, peculiar as her name, had a grasshopper's physique, favoured machine-knitted twinsets in pastel shades, curious high-heeled lace-up shoes, always had a strand or two of pearls around her neck, had dyed icecream-cone-coloured hair that showed no roots but sat stiffly on her head like a wig and twisted at the back into a bun.

In the library lesson, what you were supposed to do was, you were supposed to get a book off one of the shelves in the library and then you were all supposed to sit down as if to eat together at the big wooden table in the middle of the room, choose an illustration from your book, trace it through crisp greaseproof lunch-wrap, transfer the tracing (having scribbled on the back of it) to a plain page of paper, then colour it in. After that, you were supposed to prick neatly with a pin around the outline, making the pinpricks so close together that you could later tear the image out like a postage stamp from a sheet. Then you were supposed to smear lovely smelling Perkins Paste on the back of it and press it on to a page in an exercise book, noting underneath the title and author of the volume you'd traced it from. If you liked, you were then allowed to take the book home to read.

My father found out about this activity when I proudly showed him one of my tracings. I might as well have come home and hummed the music from *Blue Hills* to demonstrate the beauty of my voice. Words like preposterous and outrageous sprang from his lips along with gusts of smoke from his cigarette. I was bewildered. He decreed that books and library lessons should be for *reading*, that it was ludicrous to waste children's time with tracing and pinpricking, that we should be being encouraged to draw our own pictures, not trace what he called tenth-rate rubbish from other people's tenth-rate books. Anyway, what did that stupid Pennicuick woman think scissors had been invented for? he asked. It was a crime to train children to do things that could be better done by a machine.

The worst happened. My father visited the school to castigate Miss Pennicuick. He didn't tell me this. I only found out when the next library lesson arrived and Miss Pennicuick coolly told me that he'd come to see her, outlined the compromise they had reached. Library lessons continued as before for the rest of the class. I, however, was to be exempt. While all the other children sat companionably around the big dinner table in the library tracing wishing chairs with wings springing from their legs etcetera, I languished alone in an empty classroom, and "read" or "drew pictures of my own".

In fact I did neither. I just sat there in a state of paralysis and waited for the time to pass. I felt guilty because I had enjoyed tracing and colouring in and pinpricking and pasting. I'd been good at it. I didn't want to sit in a room by myself and read or do drawings of my own.

Another time when I was not permitted to do what the other children did was the time when the missionaries came. Two bright-eyed white Christian missionaries came to visit the school and spoke to the assembled teachers and children of their work in darkest Africa converting the heathen to belief in God and Christ. One of them told a story that was supposed to demonstrate their success: he'd managed to get a black man to substitute the word Christ for whatever was the name of the deity he was accustomed to revering. I thought of us and Christmas, knew my father and brothers would certainly laugh at the religiosity of these men. But I liked the strangeness of their stories, liked hearing about their adventures in other lands, and imagined my father would at least approve of the charitable aspects of their work. They made it clear it was *civilisation* they were bringing to fuzzy wuzzies along with Christ, and emphasised there were necessities many of us took for granted that the poor natives in darkest Africa lacked, hadn't benefit of. The means for achieving cleanliness, for instance. Soap.

This was where we could help, the missionaries suggested. Though we were as the song said, little children weak, we could be part of this grand scheme of civilising savage souls. What we could do was put together kits for distribution amongst these former heathens: each child could contribute what he or she could afford. So one might bring a sponge bag, one a nail brush, one toothpaste, one soap, one a face washer or sponge, and so on, each class co-operating to produce as many little sponge bags filled with civilising toiletry items as they could. Then they, the missionaries, would take this collection back to Africa and distribute them amongst their grateful flock.

How could this scheme not appeal to a generous, kind-hearted little girl like me? I was aware, of course, that some children in my class also appeared to lack soap, toothbrushes and hair shampoo, but knowing these items were available at either of the chemists or at Lenehan's for anyone to buy, I assumed *their* not using them was a moral failing. I pitied the black Africans who had no Mercer's or Elton's or Lenehan's, and was enchanted by the thought of delighting an exotic fuzzy wuzzy with the pretty floral sponge bag I had in mind. Our teacher encouraged us to suggest a list of items that might be included. I was proud of my inventiveness in thinking of shower cap, and said I would bring one as well as a plastic holder for a cake of soap.

When I explained the scheme delightedly to my parents, all hell broke loose. My father raged. Preposterous! The arrogance of these ignorant twerps! Words failed him. What words could express what he felt? He spluttered. Anger leapt from him like flames from burning paper. Meddlers! Dogooders! Patronising scum! Scorn warred with fury in his voice. He sucked audibly at his eternal cigarette, puffed smoke, let the ash drop on the carpet. Like a foreign-language speaker who addresses the interpreter rather than the person he's meant to be speaking to, my father addressed his responses to my news to my mother, counting on her to translate them into a form comprehensible to me. What the Africans need, if anything, is penicillin and sulphonamides, he thundered at her. And so on and on.

I felt hopelessly ignorant, deeply ashamed of my mistaken enthusiasm for a scheme now revealed to me as beneath contempt. I wished my father could understand how innocent, how full of good will, we'd all been in planning it, how the missionaries had seemed so ordinary, so harmless — just fat-faced men in suits, not the depraved villains he seemed to envisage. It was a relief that my mother forgave me, said You weren't to know, dear — before translating into whole and soothingly orderly sentences his exclamations and apostrophes and gasps and grunts and barks and discontinuous phrases of scorn.

He calmed down after a while. My mother made a cup of tea. My father waxed cheerful, saw the funny side of it, began to see the ignorance of the missionaries as comic as well as tragic, made me feel safe with him, sure of his superiority to the do-gooder meddlers and the teachers and the children at school. I could see he was right: the plastic sponge bag, however pretty, would rot on the docks under the hot African sun; their contents would shrivel or melt; ants would relish the toothpaste; face washers would only spread germs; people who did not have or want our kind of bathrooms were unlikely to desire shower caps and bath salts, and would not need toothbrushes if they hadn't started eating the tooth-rotting food the missionaries had so kindly introduced them to. He mockingly alluded to the fact that Nan and my mother, encouraged by the Narramundi Red Cross, had busily knitted socks and balaclavas for the troops during the war, and that these had been duly transported to New Guinea to console men dying of tropical disease. It was pathetic. It was tragic. We weren't to know, my mother reminded. My father agreed: it was those who *did* know better who were culpable, the ones who put them up to it, let them imagine they were doing something useful when they weren't.

My mother was the one that wrote the note to my teacher saying my father preferred I didn't participate in the project of donating toiletry items for the missionaries to take to Africa. She didn't attempt to say why. It was left to me to explain my about face from boastful enthusiasm to disdain for the enterprise to the other children, smug bearers of gifts of pumicestones and violet-scented bath cubes and lemon-shaped soaps. I repeated some of what my father had said, mimicked the scorn in his voice, but my scorn never sounded as convincing as his. I said that what the class was doing was like when silly women had sent hand-knitted balaclavas to send to the troops in New Guinea during the war, but all the time I knew I would have *liked* to be involved, and so I felt phoney, a hypocrite. Someone asked me what a balaclava was. I didn't know.

*   *

Although it was a state school I went to, Scripture was compulsory. We had a lesson once a week. I found myself in the C of E classes, though I knew I wasn't really C of E. Canon Power stood before the class, a thin, balding man with a head the shape of an onion, wisps of hair like a baby and a collar that circled his neck like a back-to-front white belt. He peered at us through wire-framed glasses and talked about John the Baptist. I liked the idea of baptism, upon the fact that anyone who died unbaptised would not go to heaven. That didn't worry me much as I knew we — my father and brothers and I — didn't believe in heaven and hell. Even my mother never went to church, though she had a leather-bound Bible in her dressing-table drawer, presented to her for once teaching at Methodist Sunday school in Summer Hill. But that was when she had been Nan's daughter, and ignorant. Now she was my father's wife. She had told me proudly once that Daddy said Canon Power had said that Daddy knew the Bible better than he did. She said she didn't think much of clerics. She said she'd given up going to church when she'd discovered the clergyman at Streaky Bay was a drunkard. My brothers had been christened, but I hadn't, she said. She said you didn't have to be christened or go to church to be good. So when Canon Power asked if anyone in the class had not yet been baptised, I put my hand up proudly straight away.

The effect was spectacular. Canon Power's outward assurance collapsed like a card house. He behaved like a character severely embarrassed in a book. He blushed, began to stammer, adopted a conciliatory tone, took back everything he'd said. It was quite all right for *me* not to be christened, he kept saying. I was aware that it was really my father Canon Power was frightened of, and felt pleased, scornful and cheated all at once. What if I'd wanted to be told I had to be baptised? What about me?

At home I told on Canon Power, but my father answered none of my unspoken questions. He just said *Hmp*, then lit another cigarette and disappeared to the consulting room.

" 'Baa baa black sheep, have you any wool? Yes sir, yes sir, three bags full,' " my grandmother sang. " 'One for the Master and one for the Dame and one for the little boy who lives down the lane.' " She asked me to help her wind her wool. I compliantly held my arms stiff as a doll's and she draped the skeins of wool around my hands and cleverly wound the pale blue strands into neat, round balls.

In the city, when we moved there, I found there were no sheep, black or otherwise. Not sheeps but ships, my father said, and laughed, proud of our undeniably maritime view. I started at a city school, a private school half way up a hill overlooking the harbour, one where uniforms were compulsory, where only girls went, where everyone wore not just regulation tunics and blouses, but regulation shoes, socks, bloomers, hats, gloves, badges, jumpers, blazers, ties and hair ribbons, and wore their hair in regulation ways. We were all made to look as similiar to each other as clothes could make us look, so that each of us thought the others really were all pretty much the same, thought ourselves the only fraud.

Another former country girl started in my class at the same time I did. Her name was exotic, Zöe, with the two dots over the o, and her second name was a well-known brand of mechanised plough. This would have perturbed me, had I been her. I wasn't, however. And Zöe wasn't me. Zöe was a *real* country girl, a girl from a property, knew how to ride, knew how cows were milked, was acquainted with Aborigines, knew all about horses and sheep-shearing and show-jumping, had had a pony of her own. She'd moved to the city because her parents had divorced. In my eyes, this only added to her glamour. I tried to ally myself with her – we were both country girls, I pointed out – but she ridiculed me for not knowing the difference between a filly and a gelding, successfully established that I was an imposter who knew absolutely nothing about *real* country life. It became accepted that Zöe was from a different and valuable culture, rich in its own right, special, interesting; whereas I, being a town girl, a girl who'd never even sat on a horse, was merely an inferior version of a city girl. My status in the world had plummeted to entirely unexpected depths.

I was confused, grief-stricken, no longer knew who I was, how to think about myself. Without knowing it, I'd changed. I was no longer the only girl in the class whose father was a doctor, no longer the daughter of a socialite. Since we'd come to Sydney, my mother no longer cooked cakes or gave card parties, was no longer known never to stint on the use of butter in her cooking nor famous for her Victoria Sandwich which was invariably feather-light. In Rose Bay nobody cared that Nan could knit prize-winning garments and I knew better than to mention her predilection for *Blue Hills* even as a joke. I learnt, too, that it was foolish to boast that my big brothers had dug a large swimming pool in our Narramundi backyard with picks and mattocks: people with swimming pools here had proper tiled swimming pools full of bright blue water. In Narramundi I'd had to apologise for being rich, had felt guilty for having a swimming pool at all when others lacked one, but in Sydney I felt ashamed of being poor, was mocked for the eccentricity of our ramshackle house which my father so foolishly imagined was redeemed by its harbour view. Here I no longer felt myself to be a child exempt from the otherwise universal need to be baptised.

What I missed was the *town*, Mercer's and Lenehan's and Canon Power and Miss Pennicuick and the home-made concrete-lined swimming pool full of water-beetles in our backyard and the seductive stained glass windows of the wicked Roman Catholic church — but what I thought it was *correct* to miss was Nature as portrayed in the scraps of Walter de la Mare and Masefield and Wordsworth we'd had to read in Poetry at my new school. When the class was set the task of actually writing a poem, I thought of Masefield's nostalgia for the sea and of Wordsworth's host of golden daffodils and of Zöe's even more mystifying version of country life, and I wrote "Oh, For the Country":

> How I wish I could go to the country again,
> Across the fields and across the plain.
> 'Tis lovely to be in the country, I tell you,
> With flowers and trees and Beauty all round you.
>
> 'Tis lovely to walk by the streams so blue.

When I go to the country I often do!
I'm sure you would like it if you went there too.
I don't like the city a bit, do you?

My brothers, both a decade older than me, both medical
students, idly ridiculed this effort, said Oh! and 'Tis and Lo!
in silly voices, said Hark the Poetess!, pointed out that it was
paddocks, not fields, they were called, and that the only flowers around in Narramundi had been the carefully watered English ones, roses and snapdragons and sweet peas growing in
the gardens, and plenty of people had those in Rose Bay.
They added that what I called streams were creeks and rivers, and they weren't blue either but clear or else a rather
grubby brown or blacky-green — as I would have noticed if I
had been as accustomed to walk by them as I made out. But
my father stuck up for me, was pleased. Poetic licence, he
said. He said even Henry Lawson had said *Oh*! and *Ah*! and
'Tis and so forth on occasions, quoted *Oh, who would paint a
goldfield* to prove his point. My father regarded Lawson as a
Narramundi boy, admired him immensely. My hopes of becoming once again someone who wasn't worthless revived.

Encouraged by my father, I copied this poem out carefully
into a brown-paper-covered exercise book, illustrated it with
a drawing of my own of a sapphire-blue river and pea-green
trees, and wrote underneath in best handwriting for the benefit of my biographer: "This is my first poem. I composed it
when I was in 3rd Class A at Kambala Church of England
School for Girls. My teacher was Miss Burgess. I was 8 years
old. I had recently moved with my family from the country to
Sydney, and missed the Beauty to which I was accustemed. I
was a bit of a black sheep."

My brothers giggled over that. "Baa baa black sheep",
they sang in voices considerably less tuneful than Nan's.
They made the baas properly onomatopoeic, spent days
going baaaaaaaaaaaaaaaaa at me, recalled my pet black sheep
and its fate, told me what fly-blown really meant: it meant
blowflies had laid their eggs on the sheep's skin and the mag-
gots had hatched and had been crawling around under its
wool, feeding off its flesh. My own flesh crawled at the

thought of having actually touched the wool that hid such disgusting rot.

But I knew it didn't matter what the real black sheep had been like. It had been the thought that counted. I was sure that the black sheep my father imagined and admired had been an emblem of distinctiveness and autonomy, the antithesis of the sheep in Nan's song, the bane of those who followed patterns, asked no questions, obediently did as they were asked or told, pretended to be exactly like everyone else. It was this imaginary black sheep that he had given me and that I treasured, wanted to become.

I was quite surprised when I looked it up in the Macquarie Dictionary thirty years later and found out what some people thought a black sheep was.

Childhood Days

Labumore: Elsie Roughsey

When I was born, my mother and her friends made a rough circle of windbreak for my arrival, and so my mother could be kept warm and find her baby without harm. No razor or scissors were used to cut the cord, but they used shells or bottles or perhaps their teeth. The time I came was when they started using piece of broken bottle. Cure for my navel to stop it from bleeding was an ash from the fireplace. It also was used for drying up the bleeding. Even white pipe clay, that was also used for my mother's health.

My parents were young couples but they did not speak English. They spoke languages, and most of their talks and yarns were signs and signals. Most times, when I was growing up, I lived in the bush. Wherever my parents went, they took me. But truth to say, when I write this book, I have not a slightest idea of my dear mother. Was I with her when I grew a bit older? Oh, how I'd love to know it all . . . when I could take notice of who was my father or mother.

When I was eight years old, I lived with my father and his relatives. I never saw much of my mother or at least I really could not look back from eight year downwards, from the time I suckled from my mother's breast. It's too hard for me to trace back. I think my minds were too dim to understand. But anyway I still loved to grow up. The time I was a little girl, my mother was most of the time with her relatives. My mother, she was from the south side of Mornington Island. My father was from the north side of the island. So it was so hard for me to see them both together living as man and woman should. Living amongst my people, I hardly knew of them. I cannot explain how everything went.

I shall never, never tell any stories of all those times, only the day I noticed myself with my sister May William, other two friends Vera Barney and Gertie Gammon . . . how we walked along the shores of our island, going to the mission, the mission we stood around the place wondering what's going on. Hardly anyone was moving around. Few girls and boys were in school, but I had no idea of schools yet. We played around the yard until someone gave us girls a damper for tea, and we left and went back to our camps to our people.

Everyday we four walked into the mission yard. We had three meals a day, no school, no work but just went around the place. There was no one who could come and talk to us and tell us why we were in, or no one ever mentioned to us and told or explained who was our relation by sister, auntie, uncle or other relatives, or friends. Everything was quiet . . . nothing like that we grew to learn to understand. Everything was so dull. It seems we all did not understand each other, or there was no need to, or no one could help us to know who was the nearest relation to us to keep us company. Everything went the white man way . . . quiet and lonely, also friendless. All the orders we got from the white man and his wife. After getting our damper for tea about five o'clock, we went home, back to our windbreak roughly made . . . no house, but amongst scrubs, grass and trees. As I mentioned before, about my parents I do not know, but they could have been my father's parents who looked after me at the time. All I can say . . . I was contented with who I stayed with.

Each day it happened, until there was the time when the missionaries desired to have us put in the dormitory to stay with the other children and go to school.

My big sister and brother were already in the dormitory, but we all did not know each other as families. We were only ordinary to one another, like the rest of the boys and girls who were there. I wonder why.

It's because our parents were scattered people, or it's because the missionaries and my people did not understand each other when talking to each other to find who this child belongs to, and how family comes together, so they can help the children who have been taken away from their loved ones to the mission dormitory.

I even cannot think back whether my father or mother

brought me in to the dormitory, or I was just taken in. I did not like being in the dormitory. I just had to live that life like the rest of them. There was now no father and mother to be near. I often felt sad to know my parents were nowhere near me. I had no one to take care of me. I did what was shown to me by the missionary lady. Things were so quiet each day. It was so awful.

Well, I was a sad little girl, hardly knew anyone. Times went by. I came to have a bit of sense to understand some things of the new life I now had to face. I began to play around on my own, still dim with sense. Very little I can pick up. Still don't know about sister Julie and brother Ginger. Father came in to visit his children. Father would call out Elsie, May, Julie and Ginger to come over to him. So we would all come to Dad, not realising we were his children.

So Dad would say, "This is for you, you . . ." and so on until he had given us all he brought to give us.

Then we all look at each other not knowing we are brother and sisters. We say goodbye or good night to Father, and he goes back home to his camp. Each day was the same to us to see our parents, until we became to know we were in family circle. So as Dad goes away to bush it's sad for me to know I've got no father and mother to come and see me.

But it was really a very difficult life to go through. No parents near to love us and to take care for us. My mother, I really did not know her. Living in the dormitory, I thought I only had a father, but I had no idea of having mother. Mother was nothing I have known or understood. If mother's love and care . . . was nothing I knew of.

But as I grew up, I started to go to school, worked in the gardens digging holes for the plants to be planted, watering gardens with fruit trees, vegetables of all kinds. We girls were very busy. Hot days were not meant for us to stand or sit under shady trees, but get up on your feet to go on working, until the job was finished.

I can remember working the garden . . . was so hot, so hot that while carrying water to water the plants, me and my mate would run along the hot sand, to try and get to a place where it was cool for our feet, not a shoe on, to keep the heat off. But in those days, shoes were not known to us. Working in the sun was too bad . . . often wished we could go down to the sea for bathe, but just could not. The times were so strict you could not be allowed to bathe in the sea, that you even weren't allowed to get out of the fenced yard of the mission. We had to go on each day the same, work in the sun.

We had so many vegetables here such as cabbages, radish, sweet turnips, beetroots, shallots, melons, pumpkins, rockmelons, sugarcanes, green peas, snake beans, cowpeas, bananas, custard apples, oranges, lemons, mangoes, limes, sweet corns and many others. The garden was so beautiful and plentiful. We girls and boys worked so hard to prepare the soil, and mixed the soil for all the plants that had to be seed sowed, and then replanted the young plants in different beds of ground. But all that work was in the days when it was so hot.

I can remember how we had to hoe up the ground for potatoes to make potato rows while the rain was pouring down. Others planted the vines. Others cut the length of the vine for the other girls to carry to the ones that were planting. It was a rushing job to do while the rain fell. Although it was hard to work, but we were always happy to see the work that had been done during the rain.

During very cold weather all the work had to be continued. No warm clothes were given to us to keep ourselves warm. Oh, it was too bad, but that was the way we lived and worked, because the days were not as what is today. You get too much comfort now. Everything is so good. We are just satisfied . . . how now to live, no gardening, not too many hard work, as my life time. Today, where we had gardens and fruit trees, there is now mess of grass, and it is all turned out to be just playground for school children. Now we all buy fruits that come from Mount Isa. We have so many beautiful soil here to grow all kinds, for farming and cattle grazing, but not much equipment for the work.

After morning service on a week day, we go to school. We had all Aboriginal teachers besides Mrs Wilson. I think Mr Wilson had to be with the men working things out. With him were other staffs who worked together in every way with the

Aboriginal men. There were many work to be done. Going to
school, I liked it, because it meant not too much going in the
garden to work. I liked school. I had many good funs and
laughs with my friends.

When caught by the teacher for playing instead of going on
with lessons, you are called, "Hands out", and there is a hard
whack on the hand, whether by strap, board or ruler. Getting
smack each day really meant nothing to us. As children
would think . . . it's the way you must take it. Although I did
not know the laws and rules of a white man, I knew we must
do what always happened each day, year in, year out. I really
understood the life of being in the dormitories. As I became
older, I found it was hard for everything to be fenced and
locked up in the dormitory. But that's how it went.

For breakfast we would have flour porridge with sugar and
fresh cow's milk. For midday lunch, rice mixed with meat
and vegetables of different sorts. Supper, damper, jam or
other times bullock's fat that had been melted. Bush fruits
and roots were all collected to be eaten at each day meals,
also pineapple, oranges, lemon, tomatoes, pawpaws, melons,
rockmelons, mangoes, coconuts. These even went to go
along with our meals.

So in those days, we had to be supported also by our folks,
who came in to sell all they could bring in to the mission. This
is how we were able to eat different foods to give us health.
Also dugong, turtle, fish, crabs and oysters were brought in
to us for extra feed. So at the same time, each children who
had been in the mission, we had our own parents to give us
more food such as wild honey, panja, nail fruit, water lilies –
these grow in lagoon or swamps, and are dug from the ground
– fish, oyster, flying foxes, goanna, swamp turtles and many
other kinds of roots that were good food to eat, different wild
fruits from the bush that had been plucked and brought in for
the children. This is how our old folk had to do . . . sell some
to the missionary lady, and got whatever they wanted, such
as dresses, flour, tea, sugar, hooks, line, tobacco, potatoes,
matches, cotton and needle, pins and other stuff that was in
the mission store to buy. Well, this is how everybody worked
together to keep up the extra food to keep their children

going. So it was a good idea, and that's why we children never had sores, colds, headache or any sorts of body trouble. We were healthy as we grew up.

I learnt to wash my iron plate, not with water and soap, but rubbing it on the wet sand until it shined clean, then to dry it out. I rubbed it on the dry sand to get it nice and dry, then put it away for the next meal. By doing that, I see now that was the only way to be clean. Although, some people now would say, "Gee that's a dirty way to have our plates washed", but that's how it went. You may wonder why these missionaries did not show us the right way to be clean by washing with soap and water and dry with dry clean cloth.

But anyway, we did not get affected with germs or sickness. We were healthy and strong and never sick at all at any time, only once a year, when mosquito were bad at nights on a certain season of the year. I suppose the fever we had was caused by too many mosquito. That could have affected us with fever, because that was the only sickness we had only once a while in a year. Whooping cough we had once that made us so sick. That's the only bad times we ever felt the way of being sick. Many sickness was not in my childhood days, as I can see today, where there are all kinds. Bad sickness is amongst my people, even school children, toddlers and infants are affected by strange sickness, that many of them are flown over to Mount Isa and other places.

Now at these present time you may have cold, sick, sore throats, cold in the chest, also at back, for days and days or for a year. When you get better from one sickness, all of a sudden, you fall in another accident. Perhaps another worser one. You never be free from sickness of any sort. Some sickness can almost live in a person's body. Some are lucky, who always keep themselves from being sick or keep away from those who often get sick, or from germs.

You wonder why most of these children have all kinds of trouble, especially bodily harm. Something is wrong somewhere in their body. You think not much bush food to eat . . . except the white man's tin stuff, too much tea and sugar, flour and many other food and no chance to go bush? I think that can harm them, because their parents and grandparents lived most of their life roaming bush, and many huntings were done by them.

Well, going back . . . when I got used to the mission I was about eight year old, because I was much taller to be eight year old, but that must have been the right age of that time to bring children up to the school dormitory . . . when I could understand few things.

But when I grew up in dormitory, I really did not understand many things. All I knew . . . the rules. Not all things as I should have learnt, but rules.

To get up early in the morning, the missionary lady or one of her children comes with the keys and opens the padlock, and we all rush out of the dormitory, just to be free, free as the summer's bird . . . then wash our faces, grab a stick and bucket and go down the well and pump out water from the well to fill a large tank for the day's drink, for all the boys and girls and the adults who had job to do in the mission, while the boys go out to bush and bring wood to cook all our meals. We do these jobs every morning, before we have our breakfast. We never sit around.

We have white flour porridge every, every morning for breakfast, with fresh cow's milk and sugar mixed. Also, we have to drink the cow's milk raw. I never liked fresh milk raw. I used to vomit. I never liked the taste. But at noon, when it's supper time we drink boiled cow's milk and that tastes much better. Then after breakfast we get into line, about five or six rows of us all, both boys and girls. Mrs Wilson pokes her head out of the window from the mission house to see if our plates are clean . . . stack them all on the table, then get buckets, fill them with water for to wash our hands, face and legs and head, then comb our hair, get into line when the church bell rings for service.

School is over. We have a midday meal, and are locked up in the dormitory to have a rest.

I can remember being locked up in the dormitory. I hated to lie down and go to sleep. I would lie down on the ground and chat away to my mate lying beside me. It was a verandah part of the dormitory on ground earth. The gate of the doorway was fastened with plain wire to the mission house . . . where no one can get out during resting hour at midday.

To keep us in . . . from the missionary house at one end there is a long plain wire that connected to the door or gate of our dormitory door. To lock us up, they pull a strand of this long wire to the end of the catch and hook it on. To let us free, they take the end of the wire off the catch, from the mission house, and bring it forward to release the gate. That's how we were really tied down, by that way. The way we were treated, it was like the early settlers, negroes who left their home and parents and had to be caged in a cage wire and put on ships to other places. I was told that. They were put in cages for USA. We were not far off the line. The way we were treated was the same.

Although things were hard, but I cannot understand why all these things had to be done in a hard way. I think in those days they had to keep us together, so we may do the things what the missionaries thought we might do. But today, I still just can't understand why it all meant . . . to be so tough with us.

At two o'clock, we are let out and back to school again. Three hours time, when the school is over we have to go down to the garden and water the young plants, and fill the water tank again, while the boys carry wood for the meals to be cooked. Sometimes we carry seaweeds from the beach to be put around the young plants. When there is a big job to do in the garden, boys, girls, men and women all work together, also for tilling up the grounds for different plants to be planted.

In the night, when I had to be locked with padlock on to the door by the lady in the dormitory, I had to be put in bed with someone. Well, it was so dark at nights. No lights were any-where. The place looked so dark. To move around the place, we all had to feel where we were going. Just imagine, we were like blinded person. That's how we had to face the dark-ness.

During the night some one would scream with fright or have a bad dream. She would scream at the top of her voice. All of a sudden you would hear yelling and screaming from all the girls in the dormitory, then, when the noise would die away everybody would be quiet again.

Now it's the boy's turn to scream and yell. Although they don't know what happened . . . the yelling on the other end of the dormitory by girls. They would scream too. Because in those times the adults told us too many stories of devil or spirits. That was well in our life, that fear, and that devil can take anyone away. That's why the girls and boys never could have a pleasant sleep at nights in the dormitory.

I can remember at nights I had a sister who always walked in her sleep. I would look for her then call out. She would get more frightened and run back to her bed. Not because I wanted to do that for any reason, but nightmare was not that I knew of. But the same thing happened each nights, so often. I would try my best to help my sister to see she came in the right bed, with me, but as I spoke or touched her in her hand she also would take fright.

But we both grew up in the dormitory, helping each other through her nightmare and all, until one day when I was fully grown up, everyone was evacuated because the war was now on. That's in the year 1942, when May William and myself had to stay with my uncle and auntie until my father returned from bush. Well, during the night May William did the same thing. She walked over to the window, from one room to another, then walked out of the house, standing and looking around. When I missed her . . . got up and saw she was missing from the bed. I then called out to her and saw her walking outside. I walked out to go and bring her back to bed, but Auntie Cora quickly and quietly walked up and whispered to me, "Don't touch her. She has nightmare." Then I asked Auntie why was that. Well, she said, "If you touch her, she take fright and die." Then she explained the rest of the things another day. From that on, I understood all about nightmares.

Every Wednesday and Saturday, the boys were sent out from dormitory, to learn to hunt, fish and crabbing, also to collect wild fruits, while the girls stayed in the mission and carried on with the work in the garden through the scorching sun, and watering plants, carrying black soil to mix in the hole ready for young plants to be put in, or for vegetables' seeds to be sowed in the ground, while the boys went out walkabout in the bush or along the sea beaches to learn to hunt for their own food. Sometimes when the boys were unlucky to find food to kill and eat, anything, the boys always gathered white gum fruits. That was the only easy food they could gather to eat. So sometimes each Wednesday and Saturday we would keep half of our midday meal, rice or some other small food to give our brothers and cousins.

We often felt tired from working but could not make it to stand or sit for a while. We had bosses that saw that we had to go on working . . . our movements didn't satisfy the one in charge of us, we would often get belting, either by a stick or belts from leather strip of a bridle piece. You could hear screams, yells and crying from each children in different places where the work was going on.

We could race across the plants with pain . . . two girls carrying large kerosene tin of water on each end of the stick, while the water . . . splashing out of the tin, before we get to the end of the plant. There isn't enough water in the tin, with all this frights and hiding. I had hard times, it was very tough to live with. Too much work, also too many belting, but it was all dormitory customs. There was no sympathy at all for us by anyone. They, who were in charge of us, were rough and cruel.

I can say no matter what I've done . . . breaking pineapple leaf to eat or banana leafs, potatoes' vine to eat or digging potatoes after the shoots come up from the place they have already cleared before . . . well, you hear shout from other girls calling out . . . I'm stealing or breaking some plants. I am called to be smacked. At the same time, after I am found out, what I've done . . . soon there are the other girls picking, eating green peas, snake beans, tomatoes, breaking cabbages' leaf or any thing that should not be touched. Well, you can imagine Elsie calling out, and telling on them, that they are stealing and breaking leaves. To their surprise they are called, and lay on tables and get much harder strapping with car rubber tube.

When we grew up we never hid another person whenever

they did wrong. We also told from each other. It was tit for tat
. . . some one told from each other. It was always the same
done for the other person. We were brought up not to destroy
anything.

I can remember when I was young, I saw lots of girls, older
ones, also boys being flogged with flagellan piece of motorcar
tyre, saw blood streaming from their bottoms and legs where
they'd been cut as they were flogged. They were cruelly
treated and for days they would have these wounds with red
sores. The missionaries did not care to cure or deal with the
bruises and cuts. It healed by itself. I hadn't got hit with one
of them because they could not use them on we younger ones.
It must have been very awful to use such dreadful thing on a
person's body like that. It looked cruel. I suppose a thing like
that happening was not nice, but anyway, it was the life away
from parents and relatives.

The only time I was happy was when my mother and father would come in to the mission and see me, and at morning
worship in Church, especially Sunday evenings. They were
lovely moments, because we could see and hold their hands
and were able to talk to our parents and other relatives. It was
good to see everybody come as one large family to Sunday
service. Old and young, blind and deaf, everybody arrived.
The church service was held morning and evening. On Sundays . . . no work, no fishing, washing, riding horses, working mustering cattle. Everything was kept as a sabbath day.

You people have no idea of such awful happenings in those
days. I'll never forget the hard times I had to face in life.
Sometimes things went right, but other times it was too bad
for a girl to live with. They were good times as well as bad
times. Although, through those awful days, I became to know
a lot of the situation of the mission life.

I went around making friends and helping the missionaries
wifes, made good friend with them, and offered myself to line
up the damper on the table as she would cut up the dampers
in small pieces for the children's meals. I would tell them
some funny little stories about other children, and we would
laugh about it.

Effie Lane was our cook. She made huge dampers in six

large tin trays, put them in antbed oven made by Mr Wilson and Mr Sydney and some native men. This oven was so large, and that's how our food was cooked, also bullock's rib bones and small piece of meat were cooked. Other best part of the beast meat was salted to go with our everyday meal, rice and meat. Dugong also was caught and speared and cooked in the oven. I used to hang around and help Effie Lane with the trays of damper.

I tried to do some small things . . . how to help. Sometimes if I am in the way, they chase me away, and say, "Get out of the way. We don't need your help." I still hang around until they call me back to help. I really like helping anyone, although sometimes it's a bit difficult . . . not needed.

Mrs Dougherty was my best friend, also Mr and Mrs Cain, Mr and Mrs Palmer, Mr Wilson, Mr and Mrs Sydney. I liked them, because I came to be free with them and had good fun with them. Mr and Mrs Scott were another wonderful couples. They played so often with we small children. They showed us many tricks with hand games and gave us share of their food when we went over to their house.

At Christmas time, it was one of the time we longed for so much. For months and weeks we looked forward and often counted the weeks and months. How much days and weeks for Christmas? It was one of the thing we knew that would be far more better to come, where happiness comes to all. Besides, Christmas meant so much to us. We knew the day when Jesus Christ came to earth to be born of a woman, and how exciting it was when all the stories of Christmas was meant real to us at the time. Not only for giving presents, but everything was so wonderful here.

Everybody looks await when Christmas boxes are unloaded from the lugger *Morning Star* . . . now is to be opened by the Superintendents' wifes. All kinds of toys are put on the table ready to be separated for presents for boys and girls, men and woman. Within a month's time, everything is put in a bag, ready to be hung on the Christmas tree. There were many toys of all kinds, lots of presents.

The boys and girls sang Christmas carols at night and that

too made us feel that Christmas was so near. It refreshed our
hearts and minds that we had the real feeling of Christmas.

When Christmas Eve was, we were all given fire crackers.
We came out from dormitories and enjoyed the night together. Then Magic Lantern, the old way with powder
works, was shown just in front of the office of the mission
house. One time it was in our earth floor church and school at
the same time, by the east side of the mission house, by the
tank and the bell. The screen was put up. We saw all kinds of
pictures. The first picture was of the first missionary Mr
Hall. Everyone kept quiet for a while. No one spoke a word.
There was a reverence of silence to all. Then there was others like "Ten Little Nigger Boys" and "Grace Darling" and
"Mother the Fisher's Wife" who was anxiously waiting to
see her husband come home, by the twilight on the verandah,
while rocking her baby to sleep. There was a signal from the
lighthouse. The fisherman's ship was on fire . . . and many
others . . . also the early tribes of our own people, whom we
saw in pictures, but never saw most of them in person, only
few of them.

As the pictures was over, the adults received potatoes, tomatoes, mangoes, pineapple, custard apples, melons, sugarcanes, pawpaws, oranges, pumpkins, all kinds of different
vegetables. Besides boiled tea, they carried away in billy
cans, damper mixed with raisins and sugar. Well, you can
imagine how many people lived in those times . . . were great
crowd of people, but there was enough for all. Before our parents went back home to their camps, they would give we,
their children, half of the good they got. Boys and girls would
stand and watch how things by serving went on, until all had
received. That was the custom of Christmas Eve. Everybody
was happy because it was only once a year it happened, and
that's how the missionaries kept up Christmas, to treat them
all in this way, make them happy.

During the night it was hard for us to get into bed. We
sneaked by the window of the dormitory to see what time the
Father Christmas would come. Hardly would we sleep, hoping to see the real Santa Claus come all the way from Lap
Land. We really believed he travelled all that way to see us,

with four reindeer on a white sledge. We knew that he was bringing us toys.

About four o'clock in the morning we are waken up by the Senior Girls to sing Christmas carols until daylight. At the moment, we have the spirit of Christmas. The wife of Mr Wilson would come and open the door in the morning and tell us that Father Christmas arrived last night and hid toys. There's a rush from the each dormitories . . . girls and boys racing all over the place to find the toys that Santa Claus had hidden.

Then on 25 December, what a surprise. After breakfast, the older men went out and brought in a Christmas tree. Often they sneaked in the tree and placed it in the building of our church. Trees were decorated with many pretty papers. On the tree hung present for all the people of the island. No one ever missed out on Christmas day.

The smaller girls and boys sang "Jingle Bells" and other songs round the Christmas tree, while the other people sat on the seats and watched on. We sang and danced as Father Christmas entered the door of the building and he too joined us with the dance and sing around the Christmas tree. Then Father Christmas told us of his journey from Lap Land and how cold it was to pass the snowflakes, just to come along and see all the children on Mornington Island. We really thought it was Father Christmas himself, and soon we found out it was my uncle Gully Peters. But that never minded us at all. Each year was always the same. We always took him for the real Father Christmas who was from far off country to visit us.

Everyone receives a present from Father Christmas. Then there are lot more presents in the bags. Then there are extra presents on the table. You could choose from there, as you pass the door to walk out.

So Christmas day was one of the exciting time, when everybody receives presents from Father Christmas. Besides, friends gave presents to each other. Adults come in from camps into the mission to give their present to their friend, and friends gave them too, their gifts. Times were so wonderful. Everyone was happy, sharing our presents to each other, seeing what we had received in our bags. At the same time when we smaller girls had no present to give to each other, we parcelled up a small gift to our brother or sister and friends which we received from Father Christmas.

About two o'clock on that same day everybody met at the sporting ground for sports. There were first, second, third, fourth prizes to be given to all. Everyone did well on all sports, so no one missed out on prizes. I was a good runner, always came first on straight race, also my sister May, Eva and Molly. There were other girls and boys who came third, second and fourth. Everyone got presents. We were real sports children. Then the adults were all good for running. Old and young won prizes. I can remember when my mother and Auntie Maggie won prizes. I ran to my mother to see what she got. She was in her middle age but was active. We spent many happy moments together during the sports. I can remember when Uncle Gully Peters was the best runner, also Kenny Roughsey. They were ties. Also one of Mr Wilson's youngest boy, Hugh Wilson. He often ran with them but he also came second. Then Barney Charles was good man for pole high jump. No matter how high the pole may be, that never stopped Barney Charles to lose his high jump sport. He always won first prize. But everyone who took part in all the sports, they all had prizes given to them.

I still think of those wonderful days. Everybody was happy and contented. Best of all was when parents and children met, to see and have joyable time together, after being so many days just living in the bush and not seeing their children too often.

On Boxing day, the boys went bush for holiday with their parents. The mainland boys who had no parents here, they were taken by other Lardil people to care for them, and looked after them during the holidays. The girls were kept in the dormitory, while our brothers on holiday. We missed them very much, and often longed that February month could come so soon, when we would be able to see them again.

Boys are gone out of the dormitory for one month and two week. So we miss them all. Oh, it was hard to live to understand that life. I hated to think of that life. Perhaps it meant to do with the law of being in the dormitory.

We girls have no holiday but still work in the garden. The girls are free to take a walk on Sunday evenings around the place, gathering fruits and gums. Wednesday evening we go down the beach to bathe in the salt water. We often enjoy our swim, and have such fun on the beaches making sandcastles and drawing and writing on the beach. We pick many pretty shells as we walk along the beach and give them to white friends that come our way, because they always want sea shells. So we would walk along the shores, and collect as many shells as we could for these visitors.

In my times, when I was small, we never were afraid of a white person. Our early missionaries always wanted us to come to know them, speak to them and get used to know them as well. Often I would be the first girl to go and hold their hands and chat with anyone who came to our island or mission. Of course I was in the hands of the missionary and was in dormitory. So we were able to do what we knew was right to be happy to meet up with other strangers, or people, I should say.

We had, once a year, government parties come to visit people of Mornington Island. It was another happy times, when the people had to come in from bush to welcome the parties. When Mr Bleakley and his party came off the lugger *Melbidir*, landed ashore on the beach, the old men of the tribes made a straight archway from the beach to the front line of the fence that led to the gate into the mission. The archway was formed with spears and boomerangs. It looked so beautiful . . . how the old people made a straight line, and the decoration of their weapons were painted red and white.

All lead their way in front of the mission house. Boxes are opened by the Councillors and the parties. All presents are given out . . . tomahawks, men's belts, pocket knifes, handkerchiefs, hats, shirts, trousers, blankets, mirrors and combs for the men. To women . . . dresses, hats, necklaces, bangles, needles and cottons, tomahawks, hankies, blankets. The girls and boys get their presents of lollies, biscuits, belts for girls and boys, hankies, pocket knifes.

Well, we all had a good time. The government parties really cared for us in those times. Their visits came with love.

Presents were always gifted. When leaving, everybody sang farewell hymn . . . "God be with You" or "Blest be the Tie". It was always a nice welcome and a sad farewell.

Those days, we had real good people who cared to come along and see all the black people. We often looked forward once a year for our dear friends. They were real Aboriginal government who even cared to look after us all and spent their time even to leave their homes and families, just to come along and make us feel we had friendly people like them to come to our island. Well, I can truthfully say they were the best people in that time.

I was about thirteen or fourteen years then, when all these things happened. Their going away from us . . . we were so unhappy. Often we wished their stay was much longer with us, but just could not stay. They had many other black people still to visit too. But the day they were on the island was so en-joyable time we spent.

As I grew older I liked being in the dormitory. I enjoyed the life, played so many games. I became a good runner, won many prizes on sports day, got lots of presents. My big sister, Julie, looked after all my presents. I now became to know I had a big sister and brother but it took a fair good years be-fore I knew I had a brother and sisters . . . Ginger, May, Julie and myself. Well, those days were good times. We had many funs, jokes together. My family were quiet children at first, but when we became to really settle down in this new life in the dormitory without longing for our parents, we were happy children.

My brother Ginger and myself were full of mischief. We did what boys and girls did. I would do mischievous things with all my girl friends, as my brother would do with his boy friends. Actually, I don't mean bad things, but cracking jokes and fun, touching things, breaking fruits, rooting up plants and many other small things. We did them, and not being found out. My brother would ride calfs and quiet horses when he was not supposed to. But when he was found out, each Sat-urday or Wednesday, instead of going out for day's outing my brother, Uncle Henry, Cousin Bambra, Alick Hills, they would stay in the mission on the mission house porch and ride all day in the hot sun on these wooden horses, and that was their punishment.

Things were so tough, but to me it was the custom to all who went to the dormitory in my time. Now children are free, but I was treated differently. I could not speak and play with my brother, uncle or cousins. The only time we could play and have fun was when the missionaries were not watching. Girls and boys were brought up not to be near each other. That's why most of us were in families and relation circle. We never knew that, and that's how we never respected each other as relatives to each other. We just grew up as boys and girls being under the hands of a European. We grew up to do everything, what the European's laws, rules and life was like. Although it looked good, the life, but to feel it was very tough, sad, lonesome, friendless of families' circle . . . hardly any happiness to make us feel were contented of everything nice being in the dormitory.

We were not free, even not have fun with our brothers or other relation amongst the boys. We girls had to stay in own side of the place, also the boys. Although, that couldn't stop us at all. We used to sneak to play and fight each other and have funs. Then if we were caught playing with our brothers, cousins or uncles, we were called and got a spanking from all our missionaries who came to work amongst us. Gee they were tough.

But as we grew up, things were not too hard. We began to have more fun as new lot of missionaries and staff came. Things were getting much better for us to look and understand. But the toughness of my time made me to be what I am today . . . nice, kind, helpfulness, forgiving, to be honest and not to be dishonest with anyone, to be happy. Well, all what I learnt made much different in life I'm living now. So those hard life I once had was to help me to understand so much . . . how to get prepared for when I was able to stand for myself, when I was old enough to keep control of myself. What I never knew in my girlhood days, is those awful days I thought was not nice for me to live with tough missionaries, but I was wrong to announce it. But that was so. I must speak true of that life, or perhaps I was not really wrong. It was the way I looked back upon it, was my way of looking at things. But that made me now free to really understand it all.

I'm thankful I was firstly put in dormitory. Now, when I see it all, it made me how to do everything right. Never mind sometimes we make mistakes, but we fix things up together again, with apologies and friendship.

I am thankful I had old parents, because in the year 1942, I learnt extra more from them. They thought me all above the top line I mentioned before. I did not learn most good things at all much. It was more how to work, keep rules given to me that I should do, and not to disobey, and remember them and other rules and laws of the land, and what belonged to the Christian Church. But anyway that was all okay. You can bring forth so much from the past . . . how it was all worked out, to what it is now . . . everyone does what their wishes, so free and not so happy. I mean this twentieth century is far more different than my time of life as a girl. I was well guarded by my early helpers who were able to teach me the real true life . . . how to grow up, with all I had and was done to me, and how I was able to get along with other boys and girls . . . were so helpful. Then the children of today can compare my time of learning and understanding. When I grew up many good things passed my way in life.

Sunrise and Starshine

Colin Thiele

My boyhood was rural, warm-hearted and rigorous. It was also free, open and reasonably predictable — at least until the advent of the Great Depression.

Ours was a small, sparse community which in today's terms would have been called "ethnic" or "bi-lingual". Most of the children in the little bush school I attended were second or third generation German-Australians, and the language of our parents at home, church and marketplace was still essentially German — as were the customs, festivals, books, songs and attitudes. The school was an island of English.

There were small numbers of other national groups too, the most important of which were the Irish. A Catholic O'Reilly was a volatile and yeasty leavening in the heavy Lutheran mix of Henschke, Schulz and Heutzenroeder. All were farmers. All toiled under heaven with their hands.

It was a landscape of ridge and valley, fallow and pasture. Red gums lined the creeks or survived in scrubby patches along the ranges. To us, on our way to school, the land was half-tamed, half-wild, and we liked it that way. Many years later I tried to catch its essence, and the effect it had on at least one boy in the district:

> It was ice on puddles and the fluffing of summer dust through barefoot toes; it was frost to the horizon and and frogs in the flooded cellar and, literally, possums in the kitchen. It was draughthorses straining in waggons, and early morning stars and Christmas and the stupendous cycle of the seasons. It was stallion and mare, bull and cow, boar and sow, gobbler and turkey hen, buck rabbit and doe — even man and woman. There was no need for elaborate sex education when every day teemed with copulation, conception and birth. As it also teemed with death.
>
> It was the miracle of living, and the beauty and ugliness of the world. And, above all else, it was solitude. I was alone to stand on

the hilltops, alone to see sunrise in a thousand ways, moonlight and starshine, storm and thunderbolt, snake's flash and eagle's strike, killer dog and wild cat. Alone to find rabbit kittens in burrows, hawks' nests in hollows, blue cranes in reeds, wattle buds breaking, sudden breathtaking new mushrooms in rings. Alone to think my own thoughts, enjoy my own happiness, nurse my own hurts. And, perhaps, to find my own self.

It was a rich environment in the midst of poverty, and we were aware of the richness. The seasonal regeneration of the natural landscape, the aching wind and the high sky, the beauty and variousness of wild life, were so much a part of every waking hour that we drew them up into our bones as we grew.

It was a fine backdrop for human existence. Its verities were obvious and universal, its realities clear – birth, burgeoning, growth, decline and death. Birth was midwives and swaddling, marriage was tin-kettling and roistering, farm life was thanksgiving and harvest bounty, old age was rocking chairs and memories, death was the solemn graveyard. Yet the dreaded sight of small coffins and tiny graves reminded everyone unendingly of another harvest no less constant among children – death by drowning, fire, dysentery, influenza, and the unspeakable scourge of diptheria.

There was much to be admired in the character of my forebears – a love of the soil and all that it produced, an enormous capacity for work, an unshakeable honesty that insisted on paying Caesar his due, a deep religious faith, a strong sense of family. There were Bible readings after meals, the heavy German syllables intoned like deep-throated bells; there was early rising to bird call and dew fall; there was passionate preparation for the pastor's visit on selected Sundays.

With the strengths, of course, went the weaknesses; a narrowness of vision, a stolid stubborness, a simple mindedness and a parochialism that led to schisms and pettiness.

To a growing boy who was later to dream of writing stories there was a storehouse of material on every farm and in every congregation. It was material with many facets – domestic, environmental, social, historical. Astonishingly, in all the dourness, even humour of dialogue if one had the ear to catch it.

There were hundreds of strands in the life of such a community. Perhaps three of the most dominant were morality, language and natural lore.

Morality was a guiding star. It came from the church and from the Bible, from precept and family teaching for generation after generation. Good and evil were locked in constant battle, punishment waited broodingly for all wrongdoers, retribution descended like hellfire from above. Laws for individual conduct were clear and immutable. Boys and girls growing up under these precepts were expected to become good citizens and good men and women. They were later to to go heaven. But the precepts were also cruel and harsh. Pregnancy before marriage signified a broken moral code and called down unutterable revulsion and disgust. The girl became a "fallen woman". At best she was "in trouble" or "in that way", at worst she was an outcast and her unborn child faced a stigma-ridden future. It was unlikely that she could ever recover respect in the community. A shotgun wedding was inescapable if only "to give the child a name", but even that was no absolution.

Yet to a young boy growing up in the midst of all this, eyes open and ears alert, there seemed to be strange undercurrents, generation gaps and inconsistencies. There were contradictions between seeming modesty on the one hand and Rabelaisian earthiness on the other; between the discreet rose-embossed chamber pots inside the house and the riotous young fellows lined up at night near the loquat tree outside telling ribald jokes while they were about it; between girls sitting demurely at the organ playing *lieder* and later seeking out the same communal bushes or rolling about with laughter over similar jokes in the darkness of the verandah.

This ambivalence also found expression elsewhere – in contradictions between a farmer's hymn-singing on Sunday and his thunderous blasphemy in both German and English against his teams on Monday; his conviction that cleanliness was next to Godliness, but his reluctance to take off all his clothes to wash himself. The shattering scandal of nakedness was a horror so overwhelming that where it did occur all the gross details passed into legend. This seemed astonishing to me since we spent a lot of our time plunging about naked in the local creeks.

One of the great adventures of the year was the beach picnic, an annual descent upon the distant seashore by the whole community. After weeks of preparation and a long journey by special train, we were disgorged on to the wide sand and went galloping into the water. Some of the costumes of our beach brigade were perilously inadequate, especially when made of loose, hand-knitted wool, as I once tried to show:

People were sitting on the sand in small groups, opening hampers or rubbing lotion on their arms. They pointed and tittered as Benno and Victor went by, but when the boys looked about they couldn't see anything unusual.

Presently a big man walked towards them. He wore a singlet and a pair of long shorts that came down below his knees. His chest was a barrel and his stomach a tub, and the toes on his bare feet looked like Mutter Menzel's sausages. The words "Beach Inspector" were printed on the band of his panama hat.

He stood silently in front of the boys, blocking their path.

"You're exposing yourselves," he said succinctly.

Benno squinted as he looked up, not only because the inspector's head seemed to be in a patch of white cloud and blue sky, but because the sun was on his left shoulder.

"What?"

"You're exposing yourself, boy."

"I'm what?"

"Exposing yourself – indecently."

Benno puckered his nose and kept squinting: "What's that mean?"

The inspector stepped closer and lowered his voice.

"You're putting on a show."

Benno was still looking up. "I don't get you."

The inspector was losing patience.

"Between your legs," he said tersely. "Your bathers – they're not doing the job."

The message sank in at last. Benno looked down hastily, gasped, and moved his legs together so quickly that he almost overbalanced. He blushed as deeply as the glowing sunburn on his shoulder.

"Was something showing?" he asked innocently.

The inspector fixed him with a stony look. "Everything."

Language and the variousness of human speech fascinated me at an early age. I became aware of their subtlety and variety, their range and difference from place to place, occasion to occasion. I think at least three profoundly different influences worked on me: the German of home, church and Sunday School, the English of schoolroom and textbook, and the vernacular Australian of the open road.

The German I learnt at my mother's knee and beside the kitchen table, or out in farmyard and paddock with my father, uncles and neighbours, absorbing it naturally and somewhat inaccurately, speaking nothing else until I went to school. It was already an inbred German , a kind of "Barossa Deutsch" which later gained me some notoriety at the university because it enabled me to provide the lecturers with the right answers whenever crudities or vulgarities were required in the translations. This was a distinction that would have mortified my mother.

On the other hand I had already embarrassed her monumentally several times when I was still in short pants by asking her the meaning of given words from the night's Bible readings. One, I recall, was *Hurerei* (fornication) which, it seemed to me, kept cropping up with indecent frequency. To my surprise she was greatly flustered, assuring me at last that I would find out in due course when I grew up. Needless to say I went hotfoot to the nearest German dictionary, resolving that in future I would do my own vocabulary research.

English was a delight and an adventure. My mother later stated that I set off to school on my first day speaking nothing but German and returned home that night speaking nothing but English. While the translation may not have happened with quite such knife-edged suddenness, there is no doubt that I took to English lustily.

One of the reasons for this was a humane teacher who not only carried a scarred old suitcase full of story books about with her, but who even defied the awesome edicts of the Inspector by cancelling normal lessons on wet days and reading nothing but stories to the five or six intrepid wayfarers who managed to get to school at all and who sat listening to her while we dried ourselves out before the roaring log fire. On days like that, after infinite adventures with Aladdin and his lamp, it was almost sad, at four o'clock, to have to come back from Persia to the little bush school in the Hundred of Julia Creek.

The encouragement of my teachers and my mother, my enjoyment of formal English, my urge to write stories while still at primary school, and my receipt of book prizes painstakingly inscribed "for literary ability" no doubt pushed me towards the act of writing. And so I began that long apprenticeship which writers know lasts all their lives.

Yet, important though German and formal English were to my developing awareness of language, and rich though the contrasting power of each proved to be, I think my greatest joy lay in the Australian vernacular. I am not even sure how or where I began to pick it up. Perhaps by instinct. In all the eddies and currents of daily life – beside lumping stack and railway siding, saleyard and shop counter, farrier's forge and pub verandah – I was aware of sounds that were very different from those in kitchen and schoolroom. Returned soldiers and timber cutters, young blades at dance halls and picnic grounds, old fellows at sheep dog trials, swaggies calling in for a hand-out, all seemed to speak with a language of their own – laconic, wry, understated, colloquial.

When I was thirteen or fourteen I discovered *While the Billy Boils* and sat amazed at the revelation. Lawson's outback boy milking a cow was *me*. His trials were my trials – every bucket, kick and cowyard smell. This, I told myself, was the way to make the land speak with its own voice.

And so my interest in dialogue deepened and grew – German idiom and accent. English cadence, Australian slang. But I didn't know how I was ever going to bring them all together. As I grew up I read and travelled more widely. The spirit of each place, especially in South Australia, that I came to know and love stayed with me – the Murray, the Coorong, the coastline, the Barossa, the Flinders, the outback, and Eyre Peninsula and the islands in the sea.

The distinctiveness, the individuality, of each one was real to me and remains so forever. They merge and blend with the interests and themes that have moved in me from the time of that childhood I have described: solitude, environment, endurance, character, morality, and the rich variousness of the human condition.

From the beginning, like most writers, I constantly tried to examine and interpret that condition. Inevitably I did it out of my own background and the nature of my own self I did it "for love", as they say — in my spare time. My real profession was teaching. It still is. I have no regrets about that. When the Great Depression moved across the world in the early 1930s I was squeezed out of my childhood and pushed in some blind kind of way in the direction of education. I quickly recognised the compatability between teacher and writer.

Good teaching and good writing make the same demands — perception, honesty, clarity, compassion, sensitiveness, and an abiding concern for human beings. Through language I tried to catch a little of this in various genre — poetry, drama, history, biography, fiction — even though I realised soon enough that I was all too often trying to catch the uncatchable. The same was true when I tried to write for children.

Yet, important though moral teaching and the lure of language were to my boyhood (today, God help us, they are called "individual value systems" and "personalised communication skills"), I think the most profound influences of all came from my natural environment. With freedom to roam incessantly I felt myself a part of its universal patterns and rhythms. In such a thinly peopled region, men and women sank back into perspective and were clearly only a part of a much vaster scheme of things than mere humanity.

Standing by myself day after day on a hilltop or knoll with the long fall of the valleys at my feet and the arch of a huge sky above me, I was a speck, a mote of no more consequence than an ant or a bee. I think it taught me humility, just as the solitude gave me peace.

It also showed me the incredible beauty of natural form and colour, texture and light — hawk's feather and bending bud, rabbits' fur and dead bird's claw, star flower in wild glass like a startled spider's eye, bullrushes and frogs, rosellas and ringnecks, running wind on the hillside, sunshine on ripening wheat, straw-golden stooks on the slopes. All of these, and a thousand more, became for me part of the joy and sorrow of the human heart — the struggle for meaning, the acts of living and dying.

Daily there were little moments of compassion, joy and heartache, of frivolity and hilarity, of danger, fear and contrition, of demand and endurance. And always there was the enveloping world of solitude — but never of loneliness. Although I could not have expressed it in these terms I am certain that the feelings and the responses were already there.

When, much later, I came to write books for children, it seemed inevitable that I should want to build on the things that had drenched me so wholly and deeply; that I should want to share them, so to speak, with other children, to reveal again some of the richness I felt was inherent in the act of living — especially when so many sophists of a later age were mouthing manifestos of gloom. I wanted to stand and say, "My God, look at it all", to point like Petulengro to the wind on the heath, the sun and the moon and the stars, and to reassure children that laughter and poetry and love and magic had not vanished from the earth — even in the midst of tragedy and sorrow. Of course I didn't achieve it. How many writers really reach the goals they set themselves?

I realise, therefore, that some people may think that my books for children constantly teach. If that is so, I make no apologies for it. But I hope desperately that they do not also preach. I hope they entertain and that the people in them laugh and cry and ache in their hearts with all humanity.

I am convinced that the human spirit remains unchanged though the most excruciating changes sweep the world. I believe that there is such a thing as strength of character, and that there are virtues in struggle and achievement, in hope and aspiration, in fun and laughter and the love of life. And I believe passionately in the humanness of human beings, and in the importance of that strange journey we all make from childhood to maturity.

They say that all of us have known only one child in our lives — the child we once were. Whether this is true or not, I know one ageing child who still sees clearly a long-ago world of sunrise and starshine through a boy's eyes high on the hilltops in the Hundred of Julia Creek.

Waterbag Summers and Draughthorse Dawns

Max Fatchen

In the early thirties the Adelaide Plains where I lived at Angle Vale were occupied by farmers growing hay and wheat, many of them still using horse teams and also using their rural wisdom to farm sensibly and with a strong feeling for their land.

The farming communities, many of them Methodists, found their recreation and worship in the small plain churches with sweet harmoniums and gusty singers and the adjoining halls where concerts, magic lantern shows and Sunday School anniversaries were social and religious highlights. Here performed the earnest preachers and pulpit pounders, here came the representatives from the temperance organisations to explain the ravages of strong drink, illustrated with graphic charts and posters. Here children sang their hearts out at the anniversaries as they stood on wooden tiers of platforms, watching the beat of the meticulous conductor who somehow welded childish treble and farmers' bass into tune. Here were the tea meetings – fabulous banquets of homemade pasties and scones, cakes of beguiling sweetness and tempting texture, cream puffs fat with fillings, and endless tea in sturdy cups that were almost unbreakable. It was a close-knit, friendly community and not as conservative as later generations might think.

As a solitary only child I found myself close to the countryside in the long walks home from school to our farm. I came to know the haunts of lizards and the shy brown snake; the sparrow hawk that hovered with feathered intensity above the stubble; the blue flowers that grew among the tussocks in spring; the nearby ranges dotted with trees, the railway line running at their foot; and steam trains uncoiling their untidy banners of smoke and shrieking day and night at the crossings where horses fidgeted and snorted in wagons and buggies and old cars creaked to a standstill.

There was a communion with the animals I came to know; the great draughthorses that I learnt to drive in the plough and cultivator, albeit with little skill, which the wily team translated into slow progress and crooked furrows. There were the crotchety cows with a kick like an Australian Rules forward; the amiable pigs and the calves fed from buckets. Farm life was ordered and patterned: sowing and harvest; the life and death of animals; the gritty northerly winds bringing dust and rain; the sou' westerlies bringing showers and relief.

Perhaps, as a child, I stored the highlights in my memory as I suppose most people do. There was waterbag weather as my father called it when the sun was as hot as a branding iron and the quail rose suddenly like whirring projectiles from the brittle stubble. The waterbag would swing under the great wooden tray of our wagon as the horses plodded from stook to stook of hay in the summer. It was a dusty entourage – the four horses, the stacker on the wagon laying the sheaves with a quick symmetry, and the pitchers with their long-handled forks lifting the sheaves with a fine rhythm and dropping them at the stacker's feet. Sometimes he would catch the sheaves, skilfully impaling them on the fork's smooth and shining prongs.

There was always the sparrow hawk, nailed to the sky, waiting for disturbed mice while the dog, red tongue out in the shadow of the wagon, shifted as the wagon shifted.

The waterbag was king, succour for the thirsty, sweating its coolness with the cork clamped in its porcelain spout. Everyone drank from the waterbag itself, a rub of the hand across the spout being the only concession to etiquette. It was raised by pitchfork to the stacker up on the hay trolley. Our head pitcher, old Bob, played the waterbag like the bagpipes: its flanks would shrink under his enormous suction and swell again as he caught his breath.

I was the waterbag boy. The water came from the farm's underground tank. I still think the water from this tank was some of the sweetest in the world. Different tanks had different tastes, like different wines.

Some people said dark things about underground tanks. There were hints of drowned mice and I wonder what's happened to that old brown tomcat? I would take the waterbag over the stubble to the farmhouse, the dog accompanying me after a brief pursuit of the resident hare that was fleet and dog-wise.

The pump at the underground tank hated us. It had to be primed and cosseted before it would yield water. It made horrible metallic sounds and then they would be replaced by a terrible wheezing as if it was having trouble with its breathing. At last it sent out a reluctant spew of water and then, catching us unawares, it would begin spouting like a geyser and bring a stern cry from the kitchen window, "Are you wasting water again?" Quickly I'd fill the bucket and then get a funnel to pour it carefully into the waterbag after giving the dog his ration. The dog drank with a heavy, concentrated lapping and a deep swallow that seemed to go clear to his tail.

Then back to the paddock again. The hay trolley was now a bristling castle of sheaves and straw. Old Bob was ready for another drink.

After the day's work, the waterbag was hung under the pepper tree in the house yard, refilled and brushed by the sea breeze that came limping across from St Vincent Gulf, a breeze bruised by the hot rough edges of a long summer day.

On the nearby verandah was the Coolgardie safe with a reservoir of water in the little tank at the top and small taps, that released droplets to keep the towelled sides of the safe damp while junkets and jellies set in the evaporated coolness of its interior. I often tested the jelly with one dipping finger to see if it had set.

It was pleasant on the verandah near sunset, with the breeze giving a broken-hearted sigh and feebly flapping a blind. The verandah had an old settee that had sat heavily in the sitting room for generations, supporting legions of visitors and receiving a rain of scone and cake crumbs until its patterns faded and furniture style became outmoded. Then it was relegated to the verandah, with a dip one end in the settee where the dog curled after his long day. As we get there, the safe dripping away, the stars came out over the range followed by the moon, silhouetting the gaunt skeleton of our windmill in its light.

Verandahs were a great place for country yarns and I heard one about a noted sheep breeder who became ill but was determined to cull and class his sheep. So his bed was wheeled on to the verandah, temporary yards built and the sheep passed in meticulous review while he made his decisions.

I liked the rhythm of the countryside at night. It was always the sound of our windmill that set the beat as its tail swung to catch the slightest breeze and its blades spun and the pump lugged the water up from the sub-artesian basin below the plains. The old windmill clanging in the night and the rush of the water into a tank was the kind of music cockies and kids and cattle liked to hear in a country with a dusty throat.

In the daytime the windmill tower was a challenging Everest for adventurous children, eagerly climbing and daring the blades to cut off their heads. Alarmed parents came shrieking, "Get down, get down." Farm helpers remarked nonchalantly to the old dogs reclining in the shade, "The young bugger's up the windmill again." Our windmill was a wonderful observation post. There I could see across the paddocks to the various farms, each with its distinctive clump of trees, the summer heat haze dancing over the furrows or, in winter, the advancing showers of rain veiling distant landmarks and sometimes creating the magic of a rainbow.

There were the cars on the roads, the teams in the paddocks, the cream lorry picking up its cans, the hay wagons plodding towards the Main North Road that led to Adelaide and the chaff mills in the suburbs. There was Angle Vale itself, a cluster of trees and buildings, a junction of roads and, most importantly, the only petrol bowser for miles. We called them bowsers then; now they're impersonal pumps where one self-serves and presents oneself to the attendant brooding over his computerised keyboard.

The man who operated the bowser was friendly and observant. He always peered in at the occupants of the cars and gave them a separate greeting. He had a great memory for people who were coming and going; for their destinations and departure points. Someone off to a country race meeting with a sure thing, someone with a load of turkeys for market, people going to the church guild meeting with greaseproof-paper-covered plates of scones and cakes on the back seat.

The bowser man inserted the hose in a medley of cars: small, elegant Fiats and knockabout Rugbys with Red Seal engines; Pontiacs with the head of the great Red Indian Chief staring implacably from the radiator cap at local palefaces. Sometimes the grand cars — the Buicks, a funereal Packard or a Hudson would arrive, driven by some local dignitary. The bowser man took them all in his stride: the Model T and A Fords stuttering in for a refill; the Chevrolet so reliable; the Maxwell with its disc wheels: the Essex with a radiator grille that could be closed against inclement weather, a northern hemisphere car purring along in this southern climate where midsummer set the whirlwinds spinning in a spire of dust, and three-cornered prickles lay in wait on the dusty cricket oval, ready to poison the hands of Saturday fieldsmen.

Local doctors fuelled their hard-working cars; local clergymen gave their battered wagons of salvation a drink — men of prayer who sometimes drove like the devil.

Sometimes the bowser man let me operate the pump. I clutched the wooden handle and pumped vigorously, watching the petrol surge into a kind of glass lighthouse tower at the top with fuel markings on it before it gurgled into the tank of our Dodge tourer. The Dodge had springs that would have supported a locomotive. It also had a fabric hood. Enormous draughts swept through its interior unless the side curtains of fabric and celluloid windows were in place.

From the bowser and its crossroads, ran the river road to eventually cross a laminated wooden bridge which had its own folklore.

It spanned a river mostly reduced to waterholes shaded by gums. Its green pools contained the wary yabby and a small fish called a "muddy" (with a muddy taste) which we lured with worms, a hook, a cord and a short line fastened to a bamboo rod. One of our local characters, leaning against a post, liked to soliloquise on the river road. He wore a tin dish not unlike a steel helmet on his head to protect him against the militant magpies. This infuriated the magpies but their beaks clashed harmlessly against this formidable armour. And the soliloquy went on.

Drovers with their sheep came over the bridge, with noisy dogs in attendance and horsedrawn vans, and they'd go up a quiet side road at night and stretch netting across the road to keep their sheep yarded, providing the council ranger wasn't about. The hawkers, too, came in their vans and their trucks and we children liked to clamber aboard these travelling shops with kettles and saucepans banging from the roof inside; with blouses and shoes; with pins and cotton and lengths of bright cotton material.

Another itinerant was the Rawleigh's traveller with potions and pills and cough mixtures, especially one for "congestion", something from which children suffered in winter. We also had a baker who was intensely religious. He would stop his patient horse and stand up to pray in his cart in the middle of the road. When, during one dry spell he was asked by a farmer what he was praying for, he answered, "For our souls."

"Never mind our souls," roared the farmer. "Stand up there and pray for rain."

I suppose the most famous person to walk across this bridge was the Australian composer and pianist, Percy Grainger, whose relatives lived nearby. I can still picture him striding along in shorts with his wife − they were great walkers.

The story we always liked best about the bridge concerned a farmer of hearty appetite. There had been a wedding in the hall the previous night and some of the food still remained on the tables, including the sausage rolls. The farmer, knowing this, decided to beat the women-of-the-guild caterers to the clean-up.

He consumed the sausage rolls and then went across the bridge in his dray and three horses to collect limestone. On his way back over the bridge, there was a lurch. The alarmed horses lunged forward and the farmer heard a disturbing sound. His load of stone was falling off − not over the bridge but through it.

He reached the other side safely and duly reported that the bridge planking had given way. But everyone knew that it was not the load of stone that had caused the near disaster but the extra guilty burden of the pilfered sausage rolls.

The strawberry fete in the local hall was one of the calendar events of the year. Strawberry fetes were something to which one looked forward with passion. They needed little advertising, only a notice in the post office window or a small placard in the local store. The news passed from child to child by word of sticky mouth. We salivated at the thought of it.

Some people had a knack of growing strawberries, an uncanny touch in bringing them to ripen at fete time. Security was tightened, but a peculiar code of honour existed around strawberry time. You didn't sneak around looking for the ripe ones in other people's strawberry beds. You didn't go raiding them under the harvest moon as you might watermelons, scrambling under fences and hoping that Old Shep the watermelon watchdog was in the boneland of dreams not about to fang the seat of your trousers.

The strawberry stalls were erected in the local hall. They stood in decorated line-ahead, aglow with crepe paper, coloured and crinkled. There were dishes and basins of washed strawberries, red as fire, and rows of virginal saucers and spoons. The strawberry vigilantes were drawn from burly young farmers, muscled by wheat lumping and hay stacking; gimlet-eyed women from the local guild; and Sunday School teachers with divine wrath on their side. All threw a protective cordon around the stalls while we children counted our money; the humble penny, the petite sixpence, a threepence still containing traces of an ancient Christmas pudding; and that king's ransom, the two bob bit.

Then the word passed. The picture hat of the fete-opener — had been sighted as she made her majestic way to the platform flanked by convenors. She declared the fete open amid juvenile cheers.

Sixpence then for a dish of strawberry and icecream delight. The icecream came in canisters embedded in ice in wooden barrels. The ice was slightly salty and had come from the butter factory, its freezing room frosted like an Alpine cave and its guardian looking like someone from the halls of the mountain king. Sixpence for a dish of delight. Go then outside under the gum trees or sit on the porch step and watch the moon coming over the ranges and let the icecream and strawberries slip into icy oblivion down the red slopes of your gullet.

So the canisters were empty, the strawberries gone, the dishes washed, the "in-aid-of" money counted. Strawberry-surfeited and drowsy children climbed into cars and buggies and went home. Later, dreams prompted by overstocked juvenile stomachs were achingly spectacular.

If the strawberry fete was a local highlight, the agricultural show at nearby Two Wells with bands and horses-in-action and cheap-jack stalls, with dogs and cats and pedigreed rams, and with competing cakes and hovering cooks, was truly a festival of country life. My father always exhibited a green sheaf of wheat and nearly always won first prize. This was because of his meticulous selection of each stalk and head of wheat. He would search his crop for the best growth and choose the patch for picking. We would go with his lantern and a small shears and hessian bags and binder twine when the evening was cool and the wheat recovering from the sun. I liked this adventure, holding the lantern high while my father snipped each stalk and laid it, as tenderly as a mother would her child, on the hessian sack.

There was a feeling of excitement out there in the whispering crop, the wind moving the wheat that rustled and swayed. There were the night noises of distant cars and the far-off shriek of a train. Then silence would come back until, far away from the dark loom of the river trees, came the blood-curdling bark of a fox. The stars were sharp and bright and the lit farmhouse windows, yellow eyes in the night.

My father loved these moments for he felt close to his land which he regarded as a living thing. He liked to be there in this quiet place amid the mystery of a country night when one became aware of presences one could not quite explain.

Next day, the sheaf was leaning against the side of the show pavilion and bearing the blue card of first prize. Farmers admired the heads of grain, the stalks and the flags of the wheat, while my father spoke gravely of weather conditions and the best time to sow and of all the wisdom that was farming lore.

So farming life went on. As I grew older, I left school to work on the farm, not with much success as it turned out.

But I do remember what I'll always call draughthorse dawn — when I stumbled out of bed to feed the horses. Draughthorse dawn was crossing the path of a fallow paddock to a long, stone stable. It was saluting the punctual hare, ears raised above his squat. It was the sharpening definition of river trees in the strengthening light and the daily rooster racket from neighbouring farms. But mostly it was the big draughthorses, horses with heavy hooves and a good strain of Clydesdale in them, big horses waiting for breakfast before being harnessed in the plough or some other agricultural implement.

The horses fed from mangers, each manger a compartment. The kickers and malcontents had their own stalls but even they were reasonable animals. As soon as they caught sight of my figure in the growing light, there were whinnies of recognition, a throwing up of heads, impatient blowing through velvet nostrils. There came the sound of a hairy knee against a manger, much as we bang a spoon upon the table.

The chaff shed which made up half the stable was dim. There was a smell of mice. The engine crouched in greasy immobility. The chaffcutter, whose whistling knives turned hay into chaff (and fingers too if you didn't watch it), was silent. The duty spiders were asleep in the hammocks of their webs. Bang, snuffle, neigh from the windows that opened into the mangers. Calls for breakfast. Breakfast was served, tubs of chaff with a dash of bran, a sheaf of hay for the old mare who was finicky. A soft nose against my hand, big liquid eyes and the white blaze of a great head: a horse's good morning.

Later, after my own breakfast (of fried eggs and doorstep toast), I went to harness the team, big collars set against great shoulders, big heads flung up, rebelling against bits and blinkers . . . manoeuvring and hitching to the plough. Back at the hay shed, predatory day had arrived. The farm cat returned for more mice. Those that ran outside perished in a quick swoop from the sparrow hawk. But the horses were in the plough, finally and irrevocably for the morning's work. The command given, the line of eight draughts took the tension of the swings, and the plough began to sing in its turning furrows its slow rural songs.

Long yarns on with these things past, I still sometimes rise and watch the daybreak over the ranges and remember my draughthorse dawns and life on the plains I love.

Goin' Back to Gundagai

Craig McGregor

When I was seven years old Mum packed my brothers and myself into the old Essex and set out from the coast to spend the war somewhere safe inland. She had a sister living on a wool-and-wheat farm just outside Gundagai and that's where I grew up. I remember us driving up to the homestead through rank brown thistles higher than the car, dust spewing out of the back, the sun beating down on parched paddocks and bare rocks and glinting galvanised iron sheds and wondering: Do people live here?

So this summer, some forty years after I left, I went back to Gundagai: to see my relatives and friends, and the district where, like Dylan Thomas, I squandered what seemed an endless boyhood, and to see if Gundagai had changed.

Five hours down the Hume from Sydney, and five miles from the town (not nine miles, as the song has it), I reach the Dog on the Tucker Box. There it is, as homespun and unprepossessing as ever, though these days it has shade trees and fountains around it and the statute is besieged by tourist coaches, fun rides, Dad & Dave's Snake Gully, and a souvenir shop. I've always liked the Dog, he looks like a real working kelpie, or maybe a heeler cross, and I like the way Gundagai people decided years ago to build a memorial to their pioneers and stick it, not in the town, but out in the bush where the bullockies used to camp.

The souvenir shop, which sells everything from tea towels to miniature tucker boxes, also has postcards which print a bowdlerised version of the ballad which gave rise to the Dog:

As I was coming down Conroy's Gap
I heard a maiden cry
There goes Bill the Bullocky
He's bound for Gundagai . . .

. . . but Nobby strained and broke the yoke
Poked out the leader's eye
Then the dog sat on the tucker box
Five miles from Gundagai.

But as every Gundagai boy knows, in the original, the dog "shat in the tucker box" as the final ignominy in Bill the Bullocky's day of troubles, and for thirty cents you can now buy a blue booklet which reveals *"The true story of Gundagai's dog on the tucker box"*. It's a lovely joke and one which has helped make Gundagai the most famous town in Australia – even if, on the pioneer memorial, the lid of the tucker box remains demurely closed!

The Hume doesn't go through Gundagai any longer: they've closed the 921 metre timber bridge over the Murrumbidgee River and built a new concrete one downstream called the Sheahan Bridge, after Billy Sheahan, the Labor member for thirty years, who reckoned there were more Sheahans than other voters in the district. To get to the township you go up Hospital Hill, past the cemetery, skirt Mount Parnassus, (the dusty hill at the back of the river which some imaginative bushman named after the Greek one), and there, clustered in among the peppercorn tree and poplars and lucerne flood plain and dusty saleyards and showground and rodeo ring, is Gundagai itself.

I'd forgotten how beautiful it is. It's a small town, two thousand people, single, wide main street, utes angle-parked outside the pubs, men in hats and women in floral dresses strolling under shop awnings, the bitumen melting in the sun, telegraph poles, trees standing in deep pools of shade, a sense of life slowed almost to a standstill: as typical as you could wish country towns across the breadth of the nation.

And around it, for mile after limitless mile, the classic landscape of Australia: hill country, hills everywhere, the valley and horizon, the whole world is dominated by them, an endless series of pale gold hillsides and gullies and undulations dotted with dark green trees like a Fred Williams or Brett Whiteley painting, hills which sometimes have the look of brown wrinkled skin, of a ewe's underbelly, others as clear and innocent as bleached straw. Today a half-moon, so pale you can hardly see it, hangs in the blank blue sky. Not a single cloud. In the distance, a dirt road snaking along by the river, red eroded gullies, a water trough, rock outcrops, heat haze. No wind. Only hills, and this vaulting blue sky, and a furnace sun you can't look at, and this pale moon, and cicadas and galahs singing into the stunning silence.

I drive slowly through the town. It hasn't changed much. A few new motels. A supermarket. A Chinese takeaway. The Gundagai Theatre – where Jimmy Johnson and Miss Savage used to chase the kids who chucked Jaffas, and where Aboriginal kids were kept to the front stalls, and where they used to hold gala Victory Balls – has closed. Instead there's a funeral parlour in the front window, and a Video Ranch opposite.

The railway station has closed, too, abandoned after the 1984 flood swept away the line; it still looks neat in its fawn paintwork and picket fence and pebbled platform but there are weeds growing between the sleepers and the signal box has sheets of tin nailed over the windows and the cutting is falling in; no more tearful farewells as the steam train carted children off to boarding school, and toilet rolls were unfurled along the carriage sides, and soon-to-be-homesick farmers' daughters and job-seeking sons got ready for the overnight journey to Coolac Cootamundra Harden Mittagong Strathfield Sydney . . .

But the pubs are the same: the Family, the Royal, the Criterion, the Gresham, plus the Jume and the Star over the river in South Gundagai. And a lot of the shops: L.J. Moses & Staff, with its rounded "arte moderne" facade; Ryans of Gundagai, for All Men's and Ladies' Wear, founded by the famous Morgan Ryan's grandfather, which still sells moleskin trousers ($80) and R.M. Williams kangaroo skin boots ($170) and shelf after shelf of Akubra hats of different styles (Cowcocky, Snowy River, Rink); and of course the Niagara Cafe, one of the great old cafes of New South Wales, where Vic Castrission still sits at the back of the rows of cubicles with their scalloped partitions and padded seats and teacups with Niagara Falls on them, and on the wall, a picture of the Acropolis and a gilt-framed photo of John Curtin and the story of "The night our nation's wartime leader dined at the Niagara Cafe."

Stribley's General Store with its smell of sawdust and water on bare boards, and its overhead wires along which the cash and receipts went zinging along in brass cylinders, has closed. But the Courthouse, the Post Office, the Gundagai Bakery, Gundagai Motors, the *Gundagai Independent*, the Catholic Convent, the Museum, Joe Luff's Garage and the Gundagai District Services Club are all where I remembered them. The obelisk War Memorial still stands at the end of the main street. You can still view Rusconi's marble masterpiece, a miniature clock tower containing 20,948 pieces of marble, at the Tourist Information centre.

The town looks more modern, more affluent than when I lived there. The shops have been done up, there are a lot of new houses, even though the population has stayed much the same. There are still stockmen in hats and elastic-sided boots hanging around under the peppercorn trees, but the whole place feels more middle class.

One late, lambent evening, drifting along Sheridan Street (like Byron Bay, many of the streets are named after poets: Virgil, Otway, Byron, Homer) I came across a group of teenagers sitting on the bakery steps, watching one of their mates doing wheelies in the main street on his bike. With their cropped hair and stylish singlets and easy mix of girls and boys they could have been city kids at Bondi. I was reminded of Bruce Dawe's "Provincial City".

> Saturday night, in the main street kerb,
> the angle-parked cars are full of watchers,
> their feet on invisible accelerators,
> going nowhere, *fast*.

On the road again: out past Jackalass, the shanty town I wrote one of my first short stories about (except I changed the name to Barabran), which now has a brick veneer house amid the tin sheds; out along the river flats, past prosperous homesteads and half-deserted weatherboard houses and the old one-room school, now derelict. I am heading for the bush, the real Gundagai, where I learnt to shoot rabbits on the run with a .22 and catch crows with baited traps and swim the Murrumbidgee and studied English Literature through Blackfriars Correspondence Course. The bitumen runs out but I keep driving; I am looking for the old farmhouse.

I come across it so fast I don't recognise it; I have stopped to photograph a high ridge with trees stuck to it like a collage when I realise this is it: the cabbage tree palm, the river gums aloud with galahs, the shearing shed, the fowl yard, the woodpile, and finally the homestead itself, verandahs half way around and a wire fence to keep the sheep out and that steep roof that possums lose their footing on and slide down to the ground with a thump.

Even this has changed. A new section has been added. When I was there we had no electricity, no running water, no inside toilet, nothing; there was a Coolgardie safe on the back verandah, and kerosene lamps in the bedrooms, a fuel stove in the kitchen, and a dunny out the back. And snakes. To wash clothes you had to boil up a copper in the shed, to have a drink you went to the waterbag outside. Gundagai was a day's horseride there and back. The sea was something I saw pictures of. Landlocked, I couldn't imagine anything different; I read bush novels by Mary Grant Bruce, the Billabong series, and decided I wanted to be a stockman.

Or a writer.

Now the farmhouse has hot water, power, TV, air-conditioning — life in the bush has grown easier at last. The mailwoman comes out twice a week. In the machinery shed there is a ute, a car, two agricultural bikes, a tractor, a scarifier, two daisywheel rakes, half-a-dozen other implements . . . and a canoe. No horses. The radio on the fridge brings the Wagga fat lamb prices, and on late summer evenings, on the front verandah, you can watch the light dwindle, and listen to the breeding ducks down on the Murrumbidgee, and absorb the stillness, and slowly come to realise that nothing ever disturbs this tranquility.

The people? They are like country folk elsewhere: friendly, laconic, kindly, narrow, the men burnt by the sun and isolation, the women by men and isolation. I like 'em. A childhood friend has become a real farmer, it's been hard, but his eyes glint with laughter and he's got this great sense of humour: the boy in the man.

"All Gundagai boys are good boys," Stan Crowe, the shire president, used to say. Patrick Sullivan, who took over the *Gundagai Independent* newspaper from Uncle Jim, reckons Gundagai is *not* your typical Australian country town at all; it's one where all the old country prejudices have virtually disappeared – Aborigines, migrants, they're all accepted, there's no real class distinction. "You'd be flat out telling me who's who in this pub," he says, downing a middy of Old. I mean even the Catholics and the Freemasons get on with each other.

"It's the home of the egalitarian dream," he argues with a grin. "Everybody gets on well with everyone else. Great community spirit." The council is balanced evenly between townies and bushies, but doesn't vote on issues that way. The old split between blueblood graziers and shop-owners has almost gone. "And it's a terrible drinking town," he adds, over another middy: nine licensed premises, six pubs and three clubs in a town of only two thousand people, with another two thousand out in the district.

Any faults? "It's terribly parochial," he says. "There's a quite firm belief here that Gundagai's the best place on earth." Pause. "And it's true."

Cliff Butcher, the eighty-year-old retired accountant who found Dr Gabriel's marvellous black-and-white glass negatives of early Gundagai life, some of which are in the National Library and some of which are reproduced upstairs amid the Eskys and plastic buckets and Dinki DIY sale items of Cliff's hardware store, reckons the town hasn't changed that much in the past thirty or forty years. There's been a surface modernisation, but the core remains the same.

"It's still generous, plus the charm of knowing all the local people – what more could you want?" he says. "Apart from which, people all over Australia feel they have a title to a bit of Gundagai."

Alison, seventeen, in Ryan's is not so sure. It's dead at night, there's no picture theatre, you've got to go to Coota or Tumut for a good disco, there's nothing for young people to do. Some of her girlfriends can't wait to get out of the place. Not her. She'll stay, prob'ly. "Gundagai's famous, when other places aren't. The people are friendly. And it's just the right size," she says.

The right size. Continuity. Maybe Cliff is right: Gundagai has become so well known now, in songs and doggerel and folklore and the tea-towel culture of travelling Australians, it's become an icon, a symbol of communality, a last link with a pioneering and simpler past which we know we have left behind but still hanker after.

In Gundagai, the men vote Labor and call their wives Mum and the women belong to the Red Cross.

In Gundagai, most of the people have grown up here.

In Gundagai, people chat to you in the shops and yarn in the street.

In Gundagai, the racetrack bookies' ring doubles as the showground goat pavilion, and the bookies are never allowed to forget it.

In Gundagai, the footpaths slope sideways because the town was rebuilt on a hill after the Great Flood of 1852 washed the old township away; Wagga people reckon you can pick Gundagai locals because they all have one leg shorter than the other.

In Gundagai, the Show is great and the races are a feature and they raised $50,000 for the aged hostel in two years.

In Gundagai, like Adelaide, there is this bloody big hill down the end of the main street, only closer.

Before I leave I made my way back to the range of hills where I used to ride as a kid and watch out for sheep which were "down" in the summer heat, getting them back on their feet before the crows got to them. No horse this time. I have decided to climb on foot.

Midday. Grasshoppers jump ahead of every step. Waves of cicadas, shrieking, engulf the mind. The sun beats down like an enemy, like spikes, like fire-strikes. I am trying to remember where the horse track is that bisects the ridge and leads down the other side. The grass is dry and tindery, it lies down like straw, as it was a few weeks ago when a twenty-kilometre-long bushfire ripped through near Muttama, destroying stock, homes, land, and everyone was called in to help.

It is familiar, but from years and years ago: I am conscious again of the harsh eyeball glare of it all, the heat-work, the exertion, the unremitting sense of desolation and strain. The river shines far below, there is a crow somewhere, flies, thistles rattling, homesteads like oases, sheep packed for shade under a gum tree; there is a heart-wrenching smell of greasy wool. I think of the face of the farmer I saw in a pick-up at the garage: weathered, stoical, damaged. A battler. The bush can do that to you, make you kindly and brutal at the same time. In that shocking heat and isolation the whole world seems swollen with anguish.

An hour later, however, I am down on the river flat again and a different bush emerges: there is cold tankwater, and swallows, and roses, and a Hills Hoist, and the friendly rumble of a washing machine from inside the homestead, and old yarns about neighbours and townies and growing up in the forties and fifties. The world returns to its normal size. Anyone want a cup of tea?

In Gundagai, nothing changes much. Like me, it just grows up.

The Woodheap

Jean Bedford

Everyone said that Hazel's father was a pig. Hazel and Emmy, her mother, called him "the old bastard" whenever they talked about him. "He looks like a hog, acts like one too sometimes," Hazel would say to Anne, watching him drive out of the yard in the battered ute. The girls were about fourteen then, Anne was at the high school in the township but Hazel had stayed on at the Consolidated, learning typing and book-keeping. Even that had cost a great deal of pain and effort to get Reuben to realise that she'd be of more use to him with some qualifications. Her older brother, Gary, had left school the day he turned fourteen to help the old man with the wood — he'd spent two years in Form Two because the old man would not agree to let him go on to the technical college to learn carpentry.

The family lived crammed together in a small colonial weatherboard over the road from Anne: the "old bastard" Reuben, Emmy, Gary, Hazel and the baby sister, Bunty — the only person in the world, Hazel said, who could stand him.

Reuben, Emmy and Bunty slept in one bedroom, Gary had the only other one and Hazel had an old iron bedstead against the far wall of the living room. On nights when Reuben was drunk, which were frequent, playing boisterous cards with Gary or his mates from the pub, Hazel would have to get into her nightie in the wash-house off the verandah and sneak miserably into bed, her stiff back to the room, hoping no one would notice her and start teasing. Some nights she didn't get to sleep until she could see the grey dawn shapes of her mother's roses appearing gradually in the front garden.

"She's nothing but a bloody servant," people said indignantly about Emmy, watching her cart the wood, hefting the sawn grey treetrunks into the back of the truck. They said, too, that she used her axe like a man. When Grace wanted a hen killed, for Christmas or someone's birthday, she always asked Emmy to do it — she couldn't stand the sight of the headless twitching of some Brownie or Blackie she had nattered away to for months in the garden. Emmy laughed at such scruples. She would hold the chicken firmly by the legs, cackling like a chook herself at its struggles, and kill it with one certain stroke of the axe.

Grace and Emmy had been friends over the years that Hazel and Anne were babies, but they had somehow got out of their old habit of visiting each other for morning tea and gossip every now and then. It had become too one-sided — Grace finally wouldn't go to Emmy's if there was any chance of Reuben being there, and Emmy was ashamed to always be the guest.

Emmy was a short woman, fat from childbearing, with stringy hair caught unflatteringly over her ears with clips. Yet the youngest daughter, Bunty, whose prettiness was the pride of the family, showed features that were unmistakably Emmy's. Hazel and Gary took after Reuben, to Hazel's disgust — large, black-haired and coarse-skinned — though Hazel had a vitality and for some years a prettiness of her own, too.

When she was older Anne often wondered how Hazel had managed in that house — how had she coped with puberty, menstruation, her body's secret growth in that absolutely un-private atmosphere? The wonder was that Hazel grew as people remembered Emmy had been at first — jolly and uncomplaining, always laughing, an attractive girl in her rude healthy way.

Reuben had a large block of land down the road which he cleared for the timber. There had been a house on it, possibly his family's homestead — they were rumoured to have seen better days — but gradually Reuben spent more and more of his time at the pub while Gary and Emmy took over the badly paying business.

One day, when they hadn't seen her for a long time, Hazel came over the road. Grace opened the door and the weeping

Hazel collapsed on to the nearest chair. Grace and Anne both assumed the old man had been beating her again.

"It's mum," Hazel managed to gasp. "She's sick." She took a deep breath and wailed. "She's got cancer." Grace's own face collapsed at the word.

Anne said, "But I saw her working this morning, at the woodheap. She looked all right then."

"Yes I know. The old bastard said we aren't allowed to tell her. He says it'd upset her too much. He just wants to keep her working till the last minute," she finished with vicious insight.

For the next couple of months Hazel was at Anne's house constantly. She and Anne had grown apart before this, their separate lives had begun, they had different aspirations, and now it seemed that Hazel had grown up, away from Anne — she and Grace had drawn together to protect Emmy. Grace sent cake and eggs over to Emmy, began going over herself again, when she was sure Reuben wasn't there, to drink tea and unobtrusively do the washing-up or bring in the washing or some other little chore. By now Emmy was thin and looked ill. She joked about it in her coarse way, saying it must be the change of life at last, and about bloody time too, she was sick of all that other business.

Finally she was taken to hospital, in terrible pain. It was rumoured that the last straw had been a rupture caused by lifting a heavy log. Certainly she had kept working, although Hazel had gradually taken over most of the domestic work — cooking and washing the heavy workclothes in the old trough, wringing everything out by hand and emerging, perspiring, to hang it all up in the dusty yard.

One day Anne went nervously over the road to help Hazel make up a bunch of Emmy's favourite yellow roses to take to the hospital. They were standing in the overgrown front garden smelling the lovely old-fashioned flowers when one of Hazel's cousins from down the hill came running in.

"You're wanted on the phone, Haze," he said. "Down at our place. The hospital."

Hazel went paper-white. She gave the roses to Anne and set off stolidly after the boy. When she didn't come back

Anne took them home and wrapped them in tissue paper. She wet the stems and laid them on their sides in the sink. She and Grace waited, drinking tea, for what they knew would happen.

At about four o'clock Hazel knocked on the door. She was still absolutely white-faced, her natural robustness seemed totally wiped out.

"Mum's gone," she said. "She's gone. And no one knows where the old bastard is to tell him."

She collapsed into tears and they stood over her, clumsily trying to comfort. Finally Grace made her some hot milk and they put her to bed in Anne's room, promising to call her if Reuben appeared. Grace rang Reuben's sister, where Bunty was staying. They had already heard.

When they heard Reuben's truck drive up it was dark. Bill went with Grace to the front gate to tell him. He was drunk and threatening in the headlights, until it sank in. Then all he said was, "Bugger. Well, bugger." Gary sat on the pile of wood in the truck, his hands clasped around his knees. He didn't move or say anything while Bill and Grace were there. Grace told Reuben that Hazel could stay where she was for a while but he just nodded.

"She can go to hell for all I care," he said suddenly. "No good, the lot of them. No good, only my baby girl, where is she, my baby, the only one who loves her poor old dad." He lurched uncertainly off in the direction of his relatives' house. After a hesitant look at Gary, still swaying on top of the wood, Grace and Bill turned and went inside.

Six months after Emmy's death Reuben married again – a widow who had the licence on a pub, but she made him take the pledge and turn Catholic first, which gave Hazel much malicious pleasure. She and Gary went on living in the old house – Bunty had been taken in by her new stepmother. Gary worked the land, cutting and selling timber. His main ambition was to make enough money to pay the mortgage and buy his father out. Hazel left school and kept house for Gary. She never mentioned her old hopes of being a stenographer.

One evening, coming home from shopping in the town, Anne and her parents drove past Hazel just putting down her axe and lifting an armful of wood to take into the house.

"Wait a minute," said Anne's father, a strange look on his face. He stopped the car and went back slowly in the dusk. Anne couldn't hear what he said but Hazel dropped the wood as if it was on fire. She stood for a moment looking after him as he came back to the car, her hands hanging loose at her sides, then she went into the house.

The next morning she left home and got a job in the town as a waitress in a coffee lounge, a job she kept for fifteen years, becoming a bit of a local character with her large easy laugh, and good-natured chat.

Before she left she came over with a last bunch of the superb yellow scented roses. Gary was going to drive her into town, she was going to board with an aunt. She had arranged it all.

Anne waited awkwardly with her at the roadside, saying goodbye.

"What did dad say to you last night? What did he tell you?" When she and Grace had asked him he had simply said, "Never you mind."

Hazel looked at her, there were tears running down her face. Her small blue eyes screwed up in grief.

"He said . . ." she blew her nose loudly. "He said . . . that's what killed your mother, that bloody woodheap. Don't let it kill you too."

Gary appeared in the ute and Hazel and Anne waved goodbye. They would see each other over the next few years until Anne left school and went to university, before they lost touch completely, but Anne remembered that inexplicable act of kindness of her father's for years and often wondered if she had ever understood him.

Over the Bump

Joan Colebrook

It was one year in the middle of things — certainly before I myself began to go south to the sister school of St Margaret's — that my father announced to the family that we were all going down "over the Bump", and that soon we would see how it had been done in the past, though we would go by car and not on horseback. Our aim would be to drive from Kureen all the way down to the coast at Port Douglas, to sleep the night there and, on the following day, to inspect the property he had bought on the Daintree River — that river which lay to the north of us and was reputed to be "swarming" with crocodiles. Just as our mother and father had ridden *up* the ranges over the Bump, we would drive *down* them, and so complete the cycle. This impetus to reconstruct the past had been stimulated by the imminent arrival in the north of our two older cousins, Bessie and Isabel Moffat, who had lived in Irvinebank when they were younger but had then returned to the south to go to school in Sydney. Their father had retired in 1912, and died in 1918, so that our cousins were heirs to whatever remained of Uncle John Moffat's wealth. To make this visit more exciting, they were bringing up on the boat with them their shining new Rolls-Royce, a car we naturally thought of as being "fabulous", which had an engine considered so faultless that it was practically sealed away from human hands. We couldn't imagine how this could be, because we were used to seeing our own old cars in a constant state of being repaired.

"Can *that* car go over the Bump?" we asked of the Rolls. "Surely it can't do *that*?"

"Perhaps we can leave it at the Landing?" my mother asked anxiously. The Landing was a clearing at the top of the range from which travellers could see for miles down the precipitous descent to the Mowbray Valley, and so to the distant coast.

"We'll get Harry to meet us anyway," my father said. Harry was the man who owned a little property at the foot of the range, and who rented out a team of horses which, if necessary, could be used to haul a car up over the Bump.

"And how will *we* get down, Daddy?" we asked in chorus.

"Yes, Ted," our mother demanded, even implored, "how will *we* get down?"

My father looked rather self-conscious. I suspect that there had been many occasions when his plans had not met with my mother's standards of security.

"Don't worry, Bina." He looked at her indulgently, but with a hint of a frown. "We'll cut down a tree and hitch it on to the Dodge to act as a brake. We'll leave the Rolls at the Landing. You will all *walk* down . . . and I will drive the Dodge."

Although I don't remember all the discussions held and decisions made, I remember vividly the arrival a week later of Bessie and Isabel — both in dark, elegant suits with collars of fur, blouses of georgette, and shoes of lizardskin; Bessie in a little toque, Isabel in a small bonnet-like straw hat with artificial cherries dangling beside her wing of shining hair. True to their reputation, these cousins brought extravagant presents with them — dresses from Paris and stockings from London; perfumes and scented soap and delicious underwear; books bound in leather and purses with money in them; gadgets from Fortnum and Mason, and chocolates from Belgium — all those things we could not afford ourselves, and couldn't find in Australia even if we could afford them; "overseas" presents which came at exorbitant prices and in glittering wrappings.

After the excitement of their arrival had died down, the planning began for the great journey to the coast — the collecting of suitable clothes, of sunglasses, face cream, and citronella; the cooking of picnic foods; the packing of towels, bed linen, and fishing gear. My mother got together a few bandages, a bottle of iodine, an antidote for snakebite, and, for bad sunburn, the omnipresent Carron oil. My father and brother conferred about the condition of our Dodge, which only a few years before had been the admiration of the district. Bessie, who was rather tall and plump but singularly dainty-footed, wrapped herself in a smart dust-proof cape, and Isabel found a light raincoat which she buttoned up to her chin, turning the collar up at the neck like a military uniform. The northern tablelands were a far cry from the civilisation of Sydney, and our cousins looked upon northern experiences as so attractive and so perilous that they must be dressed accordingly.

On the day we left our old wooden Fleetwood homestead, surrounded by its bright garden and green paddocks, we felt that we were leaving what was tidy and secure, that is, our farming lives for what was sultry and adventurous. For some reason I was to ride in the Rolls-Royce, and this meant that I would be in the prestigious position of being able to point out to Bessie and Isabel the landmarks they might not have seen yet, or might have forgotten − the hotel at Yungaburra, for example, which the enterprising Williams family had made into a centre for local festivities; or the revamped main street of Tolga, which had grown into a township since the days when our father had shared a timber mill there. It was here, on the edge of Atherton's boundary, that the road passed out of the scrub belt nourished by the monsoonal rains and moved north toward forest-like country, with rocky outcrops, gum trees, and occasional anthills. It was at Tolga that my father, newly married to my mother, had first seen the possibilities of commercial milling, and later bought the sawmill plant from its original owner and transported it to Kureen by packhorse and dray, to set up the Tinaroo Timber Company, which was subsequently to ship to the south great quantities of that warm-brown walnut wood that lined the walls in our oun sitting room and formed the mantelpiece that hung over the red-washed fireplace.

That day, it was at Tolga that we took the road to Mareeba (once called Granite Creek), a stopping place for the teams and the coaches, a place for the horses and mules to rest after their slow and strenuous ascent. It might seem odd that even as late as the 1920s those of us who lived in North Queensland experienced the very edge of the pioneer period. But that was how it was, so it was easy for us to recreate the flavour of what had gone before – indeed had not quite disappeared. In the 1920s the little stores in Mareeba still looked and smelled like pioneer stores, with their hunks of rope, and bags of flour, and tins of bully beef, and American felt hats, and axes, and hurricane lamps.

I know that we had a picnic lunch that day in the "dry country" and that we drove nearly all day and that it must have been dusk when we arrived at the Landing at the top of the ranges and stood for a while, with the rainy mist swirling about us, looking down at the shrouded fertility of the Mowbray Valley. "Everybody out but the lady with the baby" was a phrase we had known from our childhood; although it referred to the old coaching days, it applied now, and my father quoted it as we all tumbled out of the cars, and stood around feeling chilly while he cut down a medium-sized tree and attached it to the back of the battered Dodge. This would steady the car and act as a brake for the descent. The grade was about one in three, and the road passed over a great bulge of gray slate, slippery and perilous in the damp weather.

In the fast-fading light we watched the Dodge sliding ahead of us, and I remember saying to Bessie, "What will happen to Daddy if the tree doesn't hold, and if the car goes too fast?"

And she said, "I don't think anything like that will happen," and she tucked my hand over her arm, and we all walked down the road, our shoes sliding on the loose gravel. Someone had a lantern. The calves of my legs trembled and began to ache from the effort of struggling over the great mass of wet slate, that is, over the Bump.

As night fell, we came to Port Douglas and stood in the vast featureless lounge of the big wooden hotel, where the only concession to decoration was a nugget of gold from the early "rush" days, reposing in a padlocked glass case, and all at once we were aware of the coastal heat, of the whine of mosquitoes, of the faintly exciting smell of rank mud and salty waters.

In the morning the early sun glittered on the tin roofs and on the dark outline of a fishing boat rocking on the tide. And from the street below there came the faint jangle of bells as someone brought goat's milk to the hotel. It was into this port that boats had sailed hopefully in the early days of the Thornborough rush, long before we were born. Then there had been twenty-five hotels in the town, and two newspapers, and the population had grown to eight thousand in a matter of months. But this excitement had long ago evaporated; in fact, we engaged the full attention of the few people on the jetty as we boarded the launch that morning, situated ourselves under an awning away from the already fierce sun, and watched the captain manoeuvre slowly upstream between banks dark with mangroves, the chief product of the "black estuaries" of North Queensland. Here the mangroves, with their shining, almost lacquered eaves, formed a world of their own, into which, moment by moment, there dropped, straight as arrows, the heavy seeds that had already germinated upon the trees, and were ready to grow wherever they fell, or to drift on any tide to any destination.

The journey up the river was long and hot. Crocodiles looked like dark logs in the brown water, until suddenly, at the boat's approach, they would turn and disappear beneath the surface. The captain told how he'd been in the business once of shooting them and selling their hides, and of how at Wyndham, on the west coast, near the meatworks, there'd been what was called the "blood hole", fed by thousands of slaughtered cattle. "The gators", he said admiringly, "would swaller up that refuse . . . wise ole men they were, they'd wait to see the tide redden." He had a quiet voice and mingled disturbing details with simple science, speaking of the cold dull emerald of the creatures' eyes; and of battles he'd seen "on the mud flats of this very river, between rival males at mating time. One old chap'd beller half the night, and 'e'd reach around the neck of 'is rival an' try to chew 'is paw off!"

"Yes," he added, "they got good eyesight, and they got adjustable filaments in their throat. You see this way they close their throats when they go underwater? And they've got good hearing, I tell you. They can judge when a prey is advancing along the banks, or when humans are swimming in the water."

The mud flats around us did indeed seem alive, and all through the long hot morning the little Aboriginal boy who helped the captain would cry out, "Crikey . . . crikey, look, plenty feller today."

Late in the afternoon we reached the cottage on the property my father had bought, a low-built place, with a verandah festooned by a giant granadilla vine, its pale lantern-shaped greenish fruit hanging so seductively that my mother and Isabel were soon speaking of granadilla pie and wondering what sort of stove the cottage had. In a little while we were scrambling out of the boat, and threading our way through the tall rank grass as high as our heads and negotiable only on a wooden pathway above the slimy mud up which the water climbed when the tide was high.

I remember the white china lamp that night, swinging on a metal chain above the table with its white cloth, and the golden crust of the pie made with the seeds and pulp of the granadillas; and later, the buzzing of enormous mosquitoes outside the nets as we lay in bed; and last of all, the hoarse bark of the crocodiles down by the river. These saltwater saurians, living relics of prehistoric times, had been bred in Australia's centre when it was a vast inland sea fed by numerous rivers. Later, as the waters shrank to lake size, and the inland rivers ceased to run, the crocodiles had retreated to the river estuaries and the sea. These creatures of salt and half-salt water, with tongueless horny palates to absorb their semi-decayed food long buried in the bottom of the rivers, were easy to imagine as we lay in the dark that night. We knew also that the calves and the ponies and sometimes even the Timor cattle could be dragged down into the water and the smothering mud, and that the great armour-plated crocodile could fling itself sideways in a rotating movement called the "death roll". I could see the webbed hind feet of these animals gripping the earth, leaving long scars in the banks of the river. With strong, webless, clawed front feet they crawled in my dreams.

In the morning all seemed normal again. The sun shone,

the granadillas were as delicious as ever, and Bessie told us stories as she sewed on the verandah, every now and then mopping her rosy face with a damp handkerchief. My father cut some wood, and conferred with the man who was managing the property, and they discussed the news that cold-weather cattle were being crossed with Brahmans, which would give the offspring protection against dreaded tropical ticks. Over the rich landscape, with its luxuriant grasses, a veil of silence fell and seemed to merge again with the blue of the coastal range down which we had struggled the day before. Then, again, came that demon of insecurity that lay beneath the challenging surface of the Australian condition. The women began to talk of the last great cyclone, during which the Daintree River had flooded so suddenly that the original house here on the property had been washed away and several of the children of the couple who owned it drowned. The wife and husband managed to reach a big tree, in which they were marooned on the topmost branches – the man with a broken leg, sustained when he tried ineffectually to rescue the children. All night long the woman clung to her youngest child, whom she held in her arms while the water whirled around them. There was nothing to eat, and the only utensil they had for water was a small metal matchbox. When daylight came the man held the child, and the woman climbed down with the matchbox and returned again and again with small portions of water for them to drink. When they were rescued at last, this couple simply wanted to leave the place forever; they sold the property to my parents.

I noticed that my father looked anxiously at us as this story was repeated. He didn't like us to hear too many tales of horror. I think he felt that, as we grew up, we would need all the confidence at our disposal. Sensing this, Bessie began to tell the younger ones an Aboriginal tale about a blue-tongued lizard whose name was Bungurrah and who kept a source of water hidden under a flat stone. "Everyone was very thirsty," said Bessie, "so the little white rat called Kaaloo was asked to follow him and find out why his tongue was wet. So Kaaloo *pushed* Bungurrah and the water flowed out suddenly with a loud noise, and flooded everywhere, and all the rivers came down from the hills and the water flowed until it reached the sea." Bessie had Robin close to her, and Robin's big brown eyes stared ahead and her face wore the abstracted expression children get when they are seeing a world beyond themselves . . .

But strange and violent stories were not finished for the day, and when the old man who had been working for our father outside came in to have his afternoon tea, he stood by the stove and began to reminisce about his life in Cooktown and to deplore the fact that the town had no solid trade now and was only a port, a shadow of what it had once been.

"Why, that was a place for real-life stories, that was," he said. "Everything happened, I tell you. There was Mrs Watson. You ever hear about her? She was born in Cornwall, England, and she came here as a governess, so they said, and in the end she married a bêche-de-mer fisherman. Watson, his name was, and the two of them went up to Lizard Island — that's the island where the queer big lizards grow that scientists are so stuck on!"

Bessie, not knowing much about the history of Cooktown, asked questions. The old man went on to tell her how Watson, the fisherman, had left the island on a trip, and how, in his absence, the wild blacks had come in their canoes to the shore and speared the two Chinamen working for the Watsons; they were advancing towards the hut when Mrs Watson drove them off with a revolver.

"She took her baby," the old man said, "and she put one of the Chinamen (wounded he was, but still alive) into a half-tank, along with some provisions, and water, and an umbrella for shade, and she tried to escape by pushing off the tank on to the reef waters. She managed to pole to another island, but there was blacks there and no water to be found."

We were all looking at the old man. "So," he said, "they lived for eleven days, and that Mrs Watson, she wrote it all down. Yes, they found the notes she made in the tank with her body and the baby's. The Chinese man, he was not far off, his head under a tiny bit o' shade. They'd died o' thirst all right." He was stirring his tea vigorously. "A brave woman," he said, but our father came in and cut him short. "That was a long time ago," he said briefly. We were all silent, staring out at the tall harsh grass, and at the river glimmering between its banks.

In the evening, as we returned in drowsy silence to Port Douglas, we rubbed our faces and necks with citronella to deter the mosquitoes, watching from time to time, the pink and crimson blossoms of the marsh flowers fall and float on the water, and waiting for the moon to rise. In a way, I was glad that we would soon leave the river and its humidity and return to the cooler tablelands. I hadn't liked the story about the children and the floods, and even worse had been the hoarse rapacious bark of the crocodiles during the long hours of darkness. Now the story about poor Mrs Watson haunted us with its terrible undertones of heat and thirst.

"It's hard," protested Helen, turning her profile, as noble as our grandmother's, as she leaned her head back against the canvas of the boat. "It's such a hard life up here, in a way . . . even now . . ." Her voice trailed off.

I was thinking of the time of the flood, when the water would have stretched for miles, and the few human beings would have seemed like tiny dark objects in all that glittering expanse. So it was before, and so it would be again. The great land behind would extend inland from the mountains, on and on into the centre, and then on to the western ocean. To think of such distances made my head spin and ache and, in spite of the slow movement of the boat, the tropical heat that sometimes grows heavier just as night falls sapped the energy out of the air. I wanted to tell Helen that it wasn't only the deaths we had to worry about but also this strange vague feeling of helplessness – the empty landscape, and the great desire to forget everything, to drift, and be mesmerised, and so not to think, and to forget . . .

Our mother and father and Isabel were sitting in front of the boat talking quietly. When Helen protested about the struggle of northern life, Bessie nodded wisely, and shut her eyes behind her glasses. Then she expressed herself, with a firm innocent smile, "In the north here, children, everything is beginning; everything is waiting for you. Everything!"

Inside and Outside

Suzanne Falkiner

Sometimes the act of writing brings to mind sensations associated with childhood: warm, dry sumer mornings; the smell of newly sharpened pencils; the feel of a thin cotton shirt against bare skin; correspondence lessons with a governess, inscribing simple sums in insubstantial exercise books with green paper covers.

The more important details have faded. All that remains is a momentary image: a child at the table, unable to do her work, staring fixedly at a wooden pencil that she twists with sweaty fingers until the paint comes off on her hands. There is something she does not understand. Her mind is too taken up with the impending punishment to grapple with the problem. The words of the woman sitting opposite are blocked out. The face of the woman is not in focus. The tablecloth is yellow, coarse-textured against her bare thin arms and slightly grubby — or did the yellow tablecloth come later? A sister at the other end, unsympathetic, always able to do her sums. I stare at the pencil marks I have made on the paper until they lose their meaning altogether. It seems so important to understand. But it has not been explained. Panic closes out reason like a wall.

Outside the schoolroom in the cottage, the sun is shining on the orange trees, there is the whirr of grasshoppers, the dry smell of grass; further away, the mud-coloured creek rippling. The children belonging to the homestead have hammocks made from hessian chaffbags hidden in the pepper trees by the creek. This is where I will go when the screen door creaks open and bangs shut to set me free of the woman. The bark of the peppercorn trees is fragmented, fragrant and dark in the old trees, smooth green in the new. When cut with a penknife, pearls of sap appear like white enamel in the gouges. No angry voices now. The world could be empty of people.

There are myriad things outside the flyscreen door. In the dark recesses of the rainwater well, there are great, green frogs with golden eyes and pulsating throats that cluster on top of each other around the cool iron water pipes. There is the elusive, wriggling grab as the colony loosens little suck-ered fingers and scrambles and plops into the dark water far below. The captured frog, which blinks in the sunlight and urinates on my hand in panic. The distant black water, the water we drink in the cottage, reflecting a silver slit of sky, and rippled now by swimming frogs.

Down in the half-acre of vegetable garden, rubbing the warm leaves of mint between my fingers for the scent, I watch the dusty, guttural white hens scratch a pink talcum dusting over their feathers, smell the over-ripe tomatoes fallen sun-warmed to the ground. In the wooden beams of the stables, the swallows build deft villages of mud, rivalling those of the wasps, lining the soft insides with feathers and white down and the long, coarse hairs from the horses' twitching tails. It is comforting to be alone in the sunlight.

The flowers in the garden in front of the house are dry to the touch, dusty at the base of the petals – dry plants, tat-tered geraniums and petunias with withered leaves that disin-tegrate as the gardener crushes the stalks and pulls them out. The exotics have only a tentative hold on the crumbling, fria-ble soil. Even the orange and black butterflies are papery and dry.

Outside the garden fence is a world of dust and heat. Not gentle heat, but a hot, piercing white light that gets inside my head, makes the sweat on my upper lip turn into little beads and the sweat between my fingers turn into grubby rivulets in the cracks in the skin. A heat that bakes the earth and drains the world of colour so that all the surfaces glare back, white and sharp and dead. Even the grass is a faded yellow, the trees bleached like an old, faded photograph.

Outside the fence is an almost incomprehensible world of landscape and distances: there are relationships between time and space that I have barely yet worked out. People are almost too foreign to consider, and the physical world is infinitely interesting.

For me, distances initially involve a pattern of trucks and rutted roads; plumes of dust in the air mark distances covered. Greater distances still are represented by air journeys between the coast and the inland, city and country, but these represent a cycle of discontinuous lives rather than of separate geographical places. The more important life is the one inhabited by tall men on taller horses, bleating sheep milling in paint-flaked wooden yards, the smell of peppercorn trees, the recognition of loneliness and, as yet unrecognised, something resembling freedom.

There is an inside and an outside. The inside is a microcosm; female, threatening. My mother is now a woman in her early thirties, although this is not something that I think about. She is almost too busy to have children, yet we exist. Slim, blonde, she strides through the house in jodhpurs, jamming a straw hat on her head as she closes the door on the cool interior, enters the heat outside. Her steps quicken towards the stables, where her beloved horses wait. My father is, as usual, absent. That leaves the governess, Miss Gantner. I have blocked out her face, but as the heavy front door slams shut, she seems to smile. I watch to see what she will do next. My sister and brother are secure in her affections. Me, she brings to my parents' attention only when I do something wrong. I have half recognised already that there is something in me that draws her, as a cat to a mouse.

So that the brick and corrugated-iron buildings of the homestead and its enclosures represent a place of uncertainty, of unpredictable adult presences and summer ritual. We perform the correspondence school lessons in the cottage by the creek, cross to the homestead for meals under supervision, prefaced by the washing and inspection of hands. The governess hovers. She has a voice that becomes shrill like broken glass, nails that dig into my wrist. The outside is preferable: undisciplined, intangible in its essence.

The outside has unseen boundaries, and its cycles involve the seasons. A year is too long to comprehend. The child there is skinny, white-blonde, untidily dressed and silent.

Among the invisible workings of the outside it is possible to move freely, unsupervised and unobserved.

I start to make solitary journeys here, sometimes around the age of six, walking along the creekbanks between the grey mud and the brown water, climbing over the trunks of drowned river gums, exploring the delicate interstices of the real world. Discoveries include the elusive black-knobbed heads of tortoises around sunken logs; clutches of wild ducklings; mussel shells with pearly mauve interiors.

In one direction, a mile along the creek, is the hayshed. Beside it is a collection of dumped equipment and piles of discarded fencing wire form a half-acre of springy, metallic coils and monstrous, antique machinery. Something that verges on the fantastic exists within the wilderness. Once I am bitten by a bat there, trying to pick it up bare-handed from where it hangs sleeping in the innards of a prehistoric, rusted tractor . . .

Much further away outside the garden fence is the woolshed, where the station children sharpen penknives, setting the great stone wheels in motion and making the sparks fly in the dark recesses of the silent interior. It is quiet and vast and empty inside the woolshed.

But when the shearing is on, the boards vibrate with the noise and reverberations of the machines, the clicking of sheep's hooves on wood. An army of men with nuggety shoulder muscles labour, navy blue singlets tucked into shapeless trousers. Their hair is damp with sweat, they wipe their faces with old, thin towels that hang like limp rags on the greasy rafters of the shed. Everywhere there is the smell of dusty lanolin from the oily fleeces, while outside the huge, shady structure sheep are pulled and shoved and chivvied in the hard sunlight, and droop-headed horses with saddles of slapping leather and jingling bits shake their coarse manes.

It is then that we, the station children, claim the privilege of sharing the shearers' morning tea: heavy slabs of fruit cake; sweet milky tea in chipped white china mugs; thick sandwiches wrapped in greaseproof paper, the white bread becoming greasy and grey with the sweat of the shearers hands as they eat.

I am shy, and a little admiring. Something mysterious about their lives, as they walk back across the paddock to the low white buildings that are their temporary quarters. Ranging across the country from shed to shed in their old cars, like some mysterious gypsies. Perhaps it is just that they seem to belong together, like a set of spoons in a box. I would like to be something like a shearer, I think.

The first friend that I make, and the first foreigner I encounter, is Toong Bak, known as Willie. I see him throwing an iron bucket at a brown and white cattle dog called Lindy Lou because she runs over his seedlings. The bitch, struck in the rib cage, runs away yelping, and the vegetable gardener's face relaxes into its habitual mask of calm. I think then that Chinese men must be different from other men, that they can look and act like this.

Toong Bak patiently digs the huge vegetable garden and produces outsize carrots in enormous quantities, which he carefully washes, ties in bunches with twine, and loads on a wheelbarrow to take around the station kitchens. The first time, I approach him with caution through the long rows of cabbages and say hello. He wears black rubber boots, blue overalls and a woven straw hat from Wright Heatons General Store. His face is permanently set in a neutral expression, the lids lowered, and his onions, parsnips and carrots, turnips and cabbages in neat lines swell bigger than they ever have before in the black soil beside the creek. He waters the garden with a complex system of irrigation, and each vegetable under his care becomes a work of art.

With time, he takes my hand in his dry brown one, and I follow his rapid, shambling route around the station kitchens to take orders. Then I am told not to. When I ask why, there is silence. The adults in question look to each other to produce a reason.

"You don't hold hands with the employees," I am finally and inexplicably told.

The Christmas I am seven, he asks me if I will ask them at

the homestead for a hen from the chook yard for his Christmas dinner. "If you ask them," he explains to me in his careful English, "they will not refuse. If I ask them, they might." It seems a reasonable proposition.

Afterwards he thanks me gravely, as if I am an adult. I suppose it is at that point that I think I am his friend.

He tells me that he went out burr-cutting when he first came to Australia. In China he was a clerk. He shows me an envelope, addressed by him in perfect copperplate. Having meticulously learnt the foreign letters, he inscribed them exactly as they had been shown in the lettering book, a craft carefully mastered. Now he raises vegetables in the same way.

When he has been on the station for many years, the elder of his two wives is allowed to come to Australia, after much negotiation with bureaucracy. She is a small, pyjama'd woman with a crinkled face who walks with tiny steps. She never learns to speak English. We see her only in the distance, taking walks by herself, a silhouette with a paper sunshade. After her arrival, Toong Bak's expression remains equally bland. There is nothing to indicate that he is happier than he had been before.

I spent less time with him then, without knowing why. His wife exists in almost complete solitude in a cottage by the creek while he works. She is never, to my knowledge, able to communicate with any person other than her husband. They have shaken hands with her, the people on the station, smiled, and felt their duty done.

Afterwards, when he goes to another station, I do not remember anything of what we talked about, although sometimes they ask me, assuming I have seen something behind the mask. But I know by some instinct that they are not really interested; the questions are posed from curiosity.

I overhear them say that I spent too much time with him; it was not natural. When I naively confide this to him, his brows knit together but he says nothing.

I am on the back of a truck with the burr-cutter's kids. We are tolerated on the trucks, the station children, like the parasite fish that attend sharks. Four of us and two dogs, among the dirty stakes and gnarled roots of wood from the ploughed land. The dust and lucerne blow back in our faces as the truck jolts along the road. We are all small and skinny, dressed in an assortment of clothes to keep out the winter cold. We hear the galahs wheeling above us over the lucerne crop; a jerking cloud of bullet bodies, a sound like wooden bells, pure enough to shock the air. There is a flashing of pink breasts, and then they turn, a mass of grey receding birds against the sky. Then, as the truck passes, they settle again on a dead tree, merging with the grey wood. I can hear the scrabble of claws on the dead wood, the clicking of beaks, though in reality the tree is too far distant to hear anything above the roaring engines.

Karen, in a blue shirt and cut-down jeans, wearing two jumpers, looks like a boy. A chunky kid with a smooth face, pug nose and almost Chinese eyes. Straggly hair in an urchin cut. She has five brothers and sisters.

"The dad I've got now," she confides in me secretly, "is not my real dad." The wind blows our hair about our faces. "My real dad used to be a fighter," she says proudly. "He did the shows."

Karen's mum left him when he tried to shoot her with a .22, she says. He only missed by a couple of inches. Karen is proud of the drama of this, the way it obviously impresses me, who is so much more innocent. She tells me how one time he was drunk, and chased them all outside into the bush, and they had to hide. Up in Queensland, this was. And how he was in jail for carrying a gun on the street. He used to come home and flog their mum with a belt, and then drag the kids out, two at a time, and lock them in the shed. And then their mum would have to sneak out afterwards and let them out when he went to sleep.

On the back of the truck, Karen's stories of her family are inexhaustible. Her present dad is working on one of the outstations. One of her brothers has asthma and has to spend eight months a year in hospital. Another sister is deaf in one ear and has to have expensive operations, which is why they don't have any money. Last year, Sandy, the other one, had to have an operation on her foot where she staked herself. Karen says the piece of wood was inside her foot for a whole six months before they got it out. Now her mum says there are too many of them. Two of the kids are in homes because her new dad has sent them away. When she grows up, she is going to go and see them. When she grows up, she's going live with her real dad. She likes him better. Yet her mother has taught her how to knit multicoloured sweaters in stripes of discarded wool, and makes sponge cakes with white icing and jelly crystals for her children.

All this seems incomprehensible to me. Why does Karen's father get drunk? Why does her mum keep on having kids if there are too many? Like the inexplicable behaviour of the cook in the men's huts, a Frenchman, who at midnight rolls prune tins down the corridors, so that the stationhands lock the doors of their rooms for safety, and wait for everything to be normal in the morning . . .

In winter in the stationhands' cottages, where flypapers hang down beside the fly-spotted calendar, the mothers feed their children with Arnott's Milk Arrowroot biscuits and luke-warm milk.

I stand with them in my bulky, ugly riding jodhpurs, which have dirt ingrained in the heavy cloth. I feel self-conscious in my clothes, suddenly noticing that they have scribble marks on the knee from idle moments during the correspondence lessons. The thick waistband rucks up the top of the too-short sweaters, my mothers' cast-offs shrunk by the washing machine. The legs wrinkle because they do not stay down over the tops of the miniature elastic-sided riding boots. I am an unco-ordinated child. I walk into tables and irritate adults with my vagueness. The clothes add to my clumsiness when I am with other people. I know I am dressed oddly, but my mother hardly notices the way her children dress. I am aware that I am different from the half-dozen other children I play with.

I watch them avidly. They are at home on the patterned lino, amid the smells and cheap ornaments of their mothers' kitchens. The mothers are kind, but wary of me. I am not one of them. But it is the mothers who are less accepting than the children. When we play marbles in the red sand outside, I deliberately lose.

In the station office, there is dusty tan linoleum and a high accountant's desk, a high stool. The manager's desk, the manager's chair — a brown leather thing that tips and swings on a precarious pivot. There are calendars of prize sheep grazing on grass of an unlikely green; enlarged photographs of famous stud rams, long since dead; ledgers with mysterious columns of inked-in figures. Men discuss "business" here in low tones. The transactions of "business" are sacred. Children are not tolerated in the office, where the running of the small village of some forty people that has grown up on the banks of the creek is discussed. I slip quickly into the dusty confines of the store.

There I might be allowed to help the book-keeper fill the orders for the homestead, the manager's house, the men's quarters, the huts. Scooping brown sugar from hessian bags, piling in neat stacks IXL jam, Log Cabin tobacco, Sunlight soap, cans of Letona peaches, pears, pineapple and apricots, packets of matches, a kangaroo hopping across a map of Australia on their sides, Bushell's tea, golden syrup in red and yellow cans, Aeroplane Jelly with the words of the song on the packet, axe handles and buckets and kerosene and disinfectant. I climb the stepladder to the high shelves, memorise the contents of tin-lined bins. I put things in cardboard cartons, wanting to be useful. The book-keeper, a patient man, puts up with the assistance and has to double-check his lists.

Kevin the cook's son and I build a raft out of forty-four gallon drums and sail with the current down the creek until the leaky drums fill up with water and sink and we have to swim ashore. With mud clinging to our clothes, we are unable to return to our homes until we have dried out. I am strapped by the governess with a stirrup leather; the cook's son remains unpunished. I bear a grudge against him about this until we conceive the idea of going hunting for emus, thinking we are going to lasso them from the backs of our horses with lengths of clothesline.

By the age of nine some of the simplicity is gone, and I look for more sophisticated pleasures.

Sitting hidden on the creekbank with a cardboard carton of comic books Kevin and I have hidden in some past conspiracy, I satiate myself with vicarious adventure. There are a hundred comics in the box, their pages turning yellow with exposure to the weather, hiding placing to a colony of slate-beetles. I sort them into piles, cowboys and animals with human characteristics losing place to superpowwers and fantastic figures of science fiction. I burrow deeper into the bamboo roots and decaying leaves, staying absentmindedly immobile until my muscles cramp, ploughing rapidly through the pulpy pages.

The Phantom lopes invincibly through a sketchy black and white jungle; Superman swoops above Metropolis. Dinosaurs menace explorers in forgotten worlds. I discover in myself a greed that lasts for weeks, for the repetitive stories coupled with a secret guilt.

Then the cook's son takes the carton away to swap at school, and this way of passing the hours of the afternoon is no longer available.

But this does not happen without some obscure feeling of relief on my part. My sister and brother and I are not allowed to have comics. I sense there is something about the secret carton that is not part of the world to which I am supposed to belong. It belongs to the world of Kevin Cooper, the cook's son, and the other older boys — of chewing gum and swearing, of saying "okay" instead of "yes", and dropping the "g" on the ends of certain words.

Kevin teaches me to steal cigarettes and how to smoke. He presents me with other enigmas, while I cough nervously in the bamboos.

"How come," he says, "your dad calls my dad 'Jim' and my dad calls your dad 'Mister'?"

This silences me for a moment. "Your dad works for my father, so he's allowed."

"Why, but?"

I don't know.

*   *

Down by the bridge over the creek the ground is packed hard, with a thin layer of powdery dust on its surface. Kevin picks up a sharp, dead stick and draws fine, jerky lines.

A pear-shaped body with a circle for a head, no neck, crooked. Half moon legs. Then arms that are lines. He touches the area between the legs of the figure.

"There," he tells me.

But what about there?

I feel a panicky constriction in my body, as if it is there that I have been touched with the sharp, dead wood.

"That's where it happens."

"What?" I do not really know, so I pretend to understand.

Then, as he explains, disbelief.

Overheard, the gum trees and the sky. It is too unlikely to think about.

I Want a Shilling Too

David Campbell

It was during the late summer of that year that Janet started keeping a moneybox. The moneybox was a warm red affair from a Christmas stocking, a letterbox with a slot in the side and a strip of sticking plaster round the top where Janet had opened it with a tin opener to see how much money she had.

"Two, four, six," she counted, skinning back the plaster and herding the silver coins into her hand, like her father counting sheep. "That makes six shillings in all. When I've saved a pound, I'm taking a ticket to Sydney to visit Bert at Coogee."

Carefully, she tossed the shillings up and down in her palm so that they glinted white in the sunlight, an exciting frosty glitter that made her eyes shine and her heart turn over inside like a fish. Then she clattered the money back into its box and, in a tent of hair, thumbed on the plaster.

"But what about me?" Bill said. "I earn it too."

"Oh, you!" said Janet. "They wouldn't trust you. You haven't a head for business."

She was delighted with this remark, borrowed from their father, and had to hum a small song under her hair to keep herself from giggling; but it annoyed Billy.

"I have a head for business," he said. "You see, I have a head for business too. And if you don't give me my share, I won't go away when they ask us. Then where will you be?"

"Now see what you've done," Janet said. "You've got my hair all caught up with the sticking plaster."

But she did not seem really annoyed, and even rolled the shillings out again for Billy to hold for a minute. Holding them under his eye, each with its bearded king, and kangaroo and emu on the reverse propping up a shield, Billy was astonished once again at the ease with which they earned them. It didn't make sense. But there they were, and sliding them from one hand to the other he said, "Know what I'm going to do with mine? I'm going to buy a cattle pup."

It was as easy as that. But Janet had started fidgeting.

"Don't throw them about like that," she said. "You'll lose them. Here, put them back."

And when they were safely gummed down again and the moneybox was stowed away in the roots of the maybush and they were loitering back up the gravel path, Janet put her thin arm around Billy's shoulders and said, "We can't have a cattle pup *and* a trip to Sydney. But I'll tell you what: I'll get Bert to send you back a fishing line, or a surf flag, or even a bit of rope from the reel."

Billy, kicking stones, thought this over. What could he do with a surf flag? Perhaps he could set it up at the creek. Moodily, in self doubt, he kicked at the stones. Perhaps Janet was right and he didn't have a business head after all.

"Or Bert might even send you his photograph," Janet said.

Bert was Elsie's boyfriend. He was a lifesaver at Coogee, and was never out of a bathing costume except in the winter when he swept out a pub and threw people out the doors. He could do anything. And during the hot early afternoons the children lay about on the linoleum in Elsie's bedroom, their towels and costumes piled ready by the door, and listened to Elsie's talking about Bert.

It was a corner room opening on to their sleepout, and often Billy wandered off through the door or leant far out one of the high vined windows for a breath of fresh air; for Elsie's room smelt. It was a smell Billy always associated with housemaids, sweet and stale like pear blossom; and somehow the thought of Bert always brought the same smell with him into his mind.

"Always fidgeting and fooling about," Elsie said, licking a curl into place in the glass. "What are you up to now? Letting in flies?"

Billy laughed his breath out among the vines and said, "Seeing where the ghost walks."

"Ghosts?" Elsie said. "Stuff and nonsense! Besides, they don't have feet."

"This one did. Emmy heard it, didn't she, Jan? Up and down a hundred to the dozen; and right under this window."

"More like old Sol with a bee in his pants!"

Elsie laughed with all her young body. Emmy! Well, who'd have thought it! Then, catching herself in the glass, she pared and refined until nothing was left but a half-smile like a paper flower between her teeth.

"And so la-di-da!" she mocked. "Kiss my foot! But you never can tell."

"You can laugh," Billy said, "but Emmy heard it."

"There's ears!"

"Getting back to Bert," Janet said, defending their old cook. "Does he really sweep out a pub?"

Somehow this did not fit in with the character of the lifesaver.

"Only in the winter." Elsie powdered, with pursed lips.

"But a pub? He sweeps out a pub, like a stable boy?"

"Maybe that's where he gets his smell," said Billy.

"What's all this about Bert smelling?"

Elsie's face was innocent with astonishment. Her man was in danger, crumbling away in these children's minds. And in panic she seized the paste photograph from her dressing table.

"Smell!" she cried. "There he is, third from the right. You can't smell in the sea all day."

And indeed, Bert, third from the right, knee up, eyes to the front, marching in his costume across the white sands beneath the unfurled flag of his lifesaving club, did not look like a man who smelt. Billy wondered how the idea had ever come to him, and hoped it would never get back. He was for all the world like a smooth-running engine, the perfect hero. Engines only smelt when they got old.

"Imagine thinking that of Bert!" Elsie, hand to cheek, sat down on her stool, holding their impressed gaze. "Whoever put such a wicked thought into your heads? And as for sweeping out hotels" — for she needed to dig in — "someone's got

to do it. You wouldn't like to arrive on holiday and find pea-
nuts and orange peel all over the foyer, would you?"

Even Janet conceded, "Hotels are different."

And Billy, quite excited, cried, "Does he sweep out
Petty's, then?"

"Something like that."

"And throw the people out?"

"If they don't behave themselves."

"Wiss!"

Billy's uncles always stayed at Petty's. There were the uncles on his father's side, tall, hand-folding, shoulder-squaring
men, always being called to long-distance telephones, who
each had a formula for greeting Billy. His Uncle George, for
instance, had once surprised him burning a snail with a mag-
nifying glass. "Very interesting things, snails," Uncle
George said. And now, whenever they met, it was, "Well,
well, old chap? And how are the snails?"

Then there were his other uncles, seldom seen, mythical
men who were always riding polo ponies up the front steps in
his mother's stories, and dossing down on the billiard tables;
and although Billy felt that they were more likely to be
thrown out by Bert, he hoped very much it might be Uncle
George.

"Show me how he does it?" he cried, wide-eyed.

"Oh, like this," said Elsie and she took him firmly by the
collar and the seat of his pants. "Bert calls it the bum's rush."

And away wheeled Uncle George, all knees and elbows in
a bum's rush, out through the open door to land a belly-flop-
per on Janet's bed.

"Hooray!" cried Billy into the pillow. His opinion of Bert
had never stood so high.

But it was when Elsie took them to the creek, as she did each
summer afternoon while their governess was on holiday, that
Bert was really at his best.

The creek, cool with willows, slanted through sand at the
foot of the hill; and the children, like a rabbiting-pack, raced
off in front of Elsie and the basket, mocking and calling until
they came to the thistle patch. There Elsie passed them while

they picked their way angularly on bare toes; and by the time they reached the flat and the Chinaman's garden, the party was together, except for Babs, a tiny figure crying "Wait for me!" among the thistles.

"I dropped my towel," Babs cried. "I dropped my towel and it's full of prickles."

"Take no notice," Janet said, foot over knee, picking. "She will take her shoes off. She only does it to attract attention."

But there was an agonising wait before Babs caught up and her nose was blown and Elsie moved off again like a hen with chickens.

Oh, the pleasure of lukewarm water after the dust and the thistles! Clear as tea, it slid over the mica sand; and the children stood legs apart in midstream watching their feet disappearing beneath them. Elsie settled down with her basket in the elbow of a willow root.

"Come here, Babs," she called, "and I'll take your things off."

Billy was sent away by Janet behind the willow to change.

"Why must I always go?" Billy complained.

"Because you're a boy."

"But Babs doesn't even wear anything."

"There's not much to Babs," Janet said.

"But we bath together."

Janet's changeable modesty always seemed to work against him.

"That's different."

"There is much to me," Babs cried, bending her round golden body back in sunlight. "There is too!"

"Now then, Babs, don't be rude," said Janet, "or I won't have you in my team."

And for the next hour they marched and paraded and saved lives, Billy and Janet being Bert in turns, while Babs, between laughter and tears, played the corpse, dragged from the shallows at the end of a length of binder-twine.

"Am I dead this time," she asked anxiously, "or just full up with salt water?"

"Shut up," said Billy, on his knees, pumping. "You're unconscious anyway. Pull her tongue out, Bert; that'll quieten her. And they often swallow it."

" 'Any sand, seaweed or other matter' ", droned Janet from Elsie's manual, " 'must be removed from the mouth.' "

"Ow!" cried Babs.

"Other matter," said Billy.

Lazily Elsie watched them from the tree. The freckled sunlight splashed her body, burning holes through the thin cotton of her dress. Bert, Bert, Bert! The summer air was full of his name, and drowsily Elsie relaxed in the embrace of the willow root that was his strong right arm.

Billy dated Bert's fall from favour from the day Mr Blake appeared on horseback above the creek bank.

"Ah!" said Blake from the sky. "Having a picnic, I see."

The effect was immediate.

Elsie sprang scarlet from the arms of the willow like a startled lover; and Janet, who had ruled for that one day that bathing with nothing on was allowed, streaked for her towel and stood with it to her lips, screened from Blake while remaining naked to the rest of the world.

"It's all right," said Billy, sloshing upstream. "It's only Mr Blake."

"Only!" hissed Janet. "It's all your fault, Billy. You're always wanting to take your clothes off; and you look disgusting."

But Mr Blake was quite at ease, heeling his horse down the side bank and clattering through the water.

"Mind if I join you?" he said. "Couldn't eat my lunch. Like concrete."

Mr Blake was the jackeroo. He had arrived a month ago under a cloud, following a telegram that read: Delayed. Expect Me Thursday's Train. Love, Blake.

"Love!" their father said. "Love! His expectations for the next half year are dagging wethers."

But Blake explained that some girl had sent the telegram, a friend of his sister; bought a pipe and a fast motorbike, and looked about him.

Now, on the sand, mouth full of scone, he repeated, "Just

like concrete! How that cook makes bread like that I don't know. It's her art."

"Oh . . . Emmy," Elsie simpered, pouring tea. "She's too busy fooling around with Sol to think about bread."

Billy stared hard at Elsie, for Emmy did not fool around with anyone, unless it were God. And Blake was up sharp on his elbow, staring too.

"No!" he said. "Not our Emmy? I don't believe it."

Elsie flushed, as well she might, but she managed airily, "Oh, you've got to keep your eyes open."

Mr Blake's eyes were very wide open, gold as the eyes of a fox; and then they narrowed into laughter.

"Well, the old trout!" he said. "I thought she died years ago."

"Oh, you've got to get up early," Elsie said. "Or late, in this case."

Billy noticed that Mr Blake's laughter came out like the tea from the thermos: the sound started at his lips and then went deeper.

"Still a kick in the tail!" he cried. "Elsie, you're a discovery!"

He was still staring at Elsie, who was laughing too, her eyes running off merrily amongst the teacups and then returning, delighted with her lie.

"Elsie!" snapped Janet, coming fully clothed and haughty from behind the willow. "Watch the tea. You're pouring it all over the scones."

But Mr Blake's laughter won the day, and soon they were all making fun of Emmy except Janet, and Elsie forgot to crook her little finger from the cup and kept offering their scones to Mr Blake.

"Go on," she said. "They'll do you good."

Mr Blake ate them and Elsie smiled. It was a strange broad smile for the world in general; but when it met Mr Blake's she coloured up slowly, as if he had surprised her getting undressed.

"Well, well," said Blake, stretching and rising, "now I know where the good tucker is."

And he cantered off with the reins so tight that old Kismet reared and side stepped like a two year old.

After that, Mr Blake turned up by accident two or three afternoons a week. Elsie packed a larger basket and spent a longer time in front of her glass. So their descent of the hill was slower and Elsie's freshness lay deeper under powder. Also the children's games changed.

"Today," Mr Blake said, "we're having a long-distance cross-country race. See that willow way off up there — no, no, the far one — well, that's the turning point. On your marks, get set — go!" And he burst the paper bag that the scones had been in.

Billy ran hard and usually got back first to find Elsie and Mr Blake side by side in the elbow of the willow and the last of the tea gone. They did not seem pleased with his win, either.

"I think I like Bert best," Billy told Elsie. "I think we should get back to lifesaving."

Mr Blake had not arrived that day, and Elsie was fidgety.

"Yes," she said. "Bert was all right. Bert knew how to treat a girl."

But then she said something that Billy never forgot, because it was the last time he remembered her mentioning Bert.

"Yes," she said, "Bert was all right, but he wasn't good enough for me. He told me so himself. A man should never say that to a girl, or she'll believe him."

Never, Billy vowed, would he ever say that to a girl, no matter how she made him feel undressed.

But it was Babs who struck first, and that was where the shillings came into it.

"I think," Babs said, "I'll stay and play sand castles. It's too hot for running."

"But we've thought of a special race for you, Babs," Mr Blake said. "See those sandpipers off there? All you have to do is run around them and home."

"I think I'll stay," Babs said, filling her bucket. "I like it here."

"But, Babs," Elsie said, "sandpipers are nice."

Babs up-ended her bucket and made a castle on the sand.

"Janet," Mr Blake said, "I've decided to give a prize."

"How much?" said janet.

"The prize is a shilling, but all contestants must take part in the race. There's no hurry home."

"First or last?"

"Last is the winner, but you get the prize."

"Come on, Babs," Janet said. "There's better sand for castles up the creek."

And Babs was led off screaming while, hand in hand, Blake and Elsie stood beneath the willow, watching them go.

"But it isn't fair," Billy said. "I work just as hard as you do."

They were back to their old argument over the silver shillings — eight in all.

"Very well then, you go and tell him."

And carefully Janet drew the bucket away from the sand. "Ah!"

"I'm sick of silly old sand castles," Babs said, and razed it with her toe. "Let's all go back."

"But you haven't seen this one," said Janet, refilling the bucket.

"Well, I will go, see," said Billy. "You see if I don't." And he marched off down the creek between the high black-soil banks.

The day was hot, but Elsie and Mr Blake were under the rug, right under, so that Billy really did not know what to do. There was nowhere to knock, so he splashed heavily through the water. The rug was still.

"Mr Blake," he called, "I want a shilling too."

Silence. Perhaps they were asleep after all.

"I want a shilling," Billy chanted. "I want a shilling too."

"If you don't go away," came from the rug, "you'll get something you're not expecting."

It was then that Billy knew he had made a mistake, but for some reason he found that he was committed, he could not leave. It was like his dream. His feet stuck fast in the sand

and he heard in anguish his silly high voice piping, "I want a shilling, I want a shilling, I want a shilling too."

Perhaps it was his head for business that kept him there, or the thought of Janet, but he remembered hating himself and that silly high voice; and when the record clicked on again and Mr Blake caught him up and slapped his ear, he was glad. The ear stung like bees and he smiled. It was what he deserved.

Soon after that, the weather changed and there was no more swimming for that year. And, though it was not his fault, Billy knew that Janet blamed him for it and the loss of her shillings. Elsie was off-hand too, and for some time Billy felt just as he did after lessons about the bad kings.

The good kings made him fine and brave; but after lessons about the bad kings, he asked himself if he would have done any better, and answered that he would not. And lying awake at night in their sleepout, the possums scolding the moon outside, he saw quite clearly that he would end up like King John with the barons in charge, or like Bert, who was not even good enough for Elsie.

It was perhaps because of this that he woke one night and heard the ghost walking outside Elsie's window. The door was closed, but he heard it quite clearly — the creak of feet on gravel. In one bound he was in Janet's bed.

"The ghost!" he whispered. "Listen!"

He could feel Janet listening with all her taut thin body and, sure enough, there was the step again and the grate of the wire screen.

"It's getting into Elsie's room," said Billy. "We'd better warn her."

But to his astonishment, Janet said, "You wait here. I'll go."

She paused till all was quiet, and then, light as a ghost herself, while Billy shivered, she slipped to the door. The handle groaned in turning. As silently the door shut behind her.

For an eternity, Billy lay sweating in the cold.

What was happening? What should the king do now?

In a trance of fear, he got out of bed and walked to the door. There Janet met him, coming back.

"It's all right," she whispered. "Come back to bed."

"But Elsie! What's happening to Elsie?"

"Come back to bed."

There, giggling, Janet pressed a warm two-shilling piece into his cold palm.

"It's for you," she said. "Elsie sent it."

And, in spite of the mystery, Billy slept soundly all that night, for he knew that he was forgiven.

Notes on Contributors

JEAN BEDFORD was born in Cambridge, England and as a child moved with her family to the Australian country. She has been a journalist and teacher, and has published short stories and the novel *Sister Kate*.

ALEX BUZO was born in Sydney, brought up in Armidale in northern New South Wales, and now lives in Sydney. For many years he was best known as a playwright (*Norm and Ahmed, Rooted, Macquarie, Coralie Lansdowne Says No* etc). In recent years he has been publishing comic novels, of which the latest is *Prue Flies North*.

DAVID CAMPBELL (1915-1979) was born on Ellerslie station near Adelong, New South Wales. He was educated in Sydney and at Cambridge, England. He was a pilot in the RAAF in the Second World War and won the DFC and Bar. After the war he farmed on various properties around Canberra and became known as one of Australia's finest poets. He published a number of short stories, mainly about children on a sheep station.

JOAN COLEBROOK was born in a house built by her pioneering ancestors on the Atherton Tableland in Queensland and has lived in the United States since 1940. She wrote the story of her Australian childhood in *A House of Trees*.

MARGARET COOMBS grew up in country towns in New South Wales before moving to Sydney. After studying at Sydney University, she spent some years in England where she travelled with circuses. In 1988 she published a book of stories, *Regards to the Czar*. She now lives in Sydney.

SUZANNE FALKINER grew up in the country in the central west of New South Wales. She has travelled extensively and draws material for her work both from Australia and overseas. She published *Rain in the Distance* in 1986. She lives in Sydney.

MAX FATCHEN was born on a farm in the country north of Adelaide. He served in the Second World War and then became a journalist. He is best known as a writer of humorous verse and as a writer for children. His work is represented in more than sixty anthologies around the world. He lives in Smithfield, north of Adelaide.

PHYLLIS GANT, who was born in Australia in 1922, lives in New Zealand. Since her first work of fiction, *Islands*, she has written another novel, a play and collections for schools. She has worked also as an editor and columnist.

DOROTHY HEWETT spent her childhood in Western Australia and now lives in Sydney. She has had a long and successful career as a poet, playwright and novelist. Her latest book of prose is the autobiography *Wild Card*.

SUSAN JOHNSON was born in Brisbane and grew up in Sydney before moving at fifteen to the Queensland bush. Her first novel, *Messages from Chaos*, was followed recently by another, *Flying Lessons*. She now lives overseas and is working on a third novel.

RUBY LANGFORD was born on the Box Ridge Mission, Coraki, on the north coast of New South Wales and attended high school in Casino. She has lived in the bush around Coonabarabran and in Sydney and has raised nine children. She is a qualified clothing machinist.

ROGER McDONALD, who lives near Braidwood in New South Wales, is the author of several novels including *1915, Slipstream* and, most recently, *Rough Wallaby*. He is the editor of *Gone Bush* and is currently writing about working as a cook in the shearing industry.

CRAIG McGREGOR was born at Jamberoo, New South Wales, and began his career as a journalist at sixteen with the *Sydney Morning Herald*. He has written fiction, studies of Australian society and essays on popular culture and music. He lives at Bondi Junction and is associate professor at the University of Technology, Sydney.

SALLY McINERNEY was born and raised on farms in New South Wales before moving to Sydney, where she still lives. She writes regularly on children's literature for the *Sydney Morning Herald*.

GILLIAN MEARS grew up on the north coast of New South Wales and now lives in Grafton. She has published *Fineflour*, a collection of stories, and has been in Africa on a New South Wales Arts Fellowship, working on a novel. She won the 1990 Vogel/Australian Literary Award with *The Mint Lawn*.

IAN MOFFITT was born in Sydney and grew up in New South Wales country towns that included Taree and Glenbrook. In 1978 he gave up a distinguished career as a journalist to write books full time. Among these are several thrillers (he has been called the Australian John le Carre) and a collection of articles, *Deadlines*.

DON MUNDAY migrated with his family from Britain to Australia when he was six, in 1909. They settled on an uncleared block of land of five hundred hectares, east of Wickepin, in Western Australia. Within two years Don's father died, leaving his widow with seven children. By 1931 Munday was shearing champion of Western Australia; his record of eighty seconds for a sheep still stands. Don Munday has published an autobiography, *Tin Dog, Damper and Dust*. He lives in Perth.

ELSIE ROUGHSEY was born on Mornington Island in the Gulf of Carpentaria of the Lardil tribe; her parents called her Labumore after the fruit of a native plant. From the age of eight she was raised in a mission dormitory but in the war years was able to rejoin her people. She has worked as a nursing assistant and teacher aid. She married the author-artist Dick Roughsey. She has published *An Aboriginal Mother Tells of the Old and the New.*

PETER SKRZYNECKI was born in Germany and came to Australia at the age of four in 1949. He is a graduate of the universities of New England and Sydney. He has published several volumes of poetry as well as fiction and has also edited a volume of multicultural writing in Australia. He lives in Sydney.

COLIN THIELE was born of German migrant stock on a farm near Eudunda, South Australia. He served with the RAAF in the Second World War. After some years of teaching in high schools he became principal and then director of the Wattle Park Teachers College in Adelaide. He has published more than fifty books of poetry, essays and fiction for children and adults. His best-known book is probably *Storm Boy* (1963) which was made into a successful film in 1976. He lives in Adelaide.